D0363458

THE COST OF TRUCKING:
ECONOMETRIC ANALYSIS

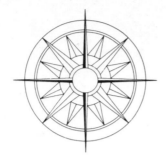

THE COST OF TRUCKING: ECONOMETRIC ANALYSIS

M. L. Burstein
University of Birmingham

A. Victor Cabot
Northwestern University

John W. Egan
University of Chicago

Arthur P. Hurter, Jr.
Northwestern University

Stanley L. Warner
Claremont Graduate School

Research performed for
The Transportation Center
at Northwestern University

WM. C. BROWN COMPANY PUBLISHERS
135 SOUTH LOCUST STREET • DUBUQUE, IOWA 52003

Manufactured by WM. C. BROWN CO. INC., Dubuque, Iowa
Printed in U. S. A.

Preface

In the recent past, there has been a great deal of discussion about the use of proprietary trucking. These discussions have been concerned, in the main, with its effect on the viability of the for-hire carrier industry. Much of this discourse has been based on very casual observation of the real situation.

The first volume in a two part study, entitled *The Economics of Private Truck Transportation*,[1] provided data and analysis aimed at making possible a more factual discussion of the private carriage phenomenon. The three papers presented in this second volume, *The Cost of Trucking: Econometric Analysis,* provide additional data and analysis on one particular aspect of mode selection, the cost.

The first of the three papers deals with common carrier trucking costs for a group of class 1 carriers. The major purpose of this paper is the estimation of relationships between the average cost of trucking per unit of output and the size of the trucking firm. In addition, relationships between size of firm and individual cost components and size of firm and profit as measured by the operating ratio are discussed. The statistical method employed is a least squares procedure with corrections for measurement errors.

The second paper is concerned with the equipment scheduling problem of both common and private carriers. Various aspects of

---

[1]Walter Y. Oi and Arthur P. Hurter, Jr., *The Economics of Private Truck Transportation* (Dubuque: Wm. C. Brown Co., 1965).

scheduling over time are considered, including vehicle maintenance and driver scheduling problems. Appropriate truck "rentals" are established and the total cost of making a particular shipment is computed. Finally computational problems are discussed.

The third paper is a detailed case study of the shipping operation of a large commercial grocer. This firm makes transcontinental shipments of commodities, as well as shorter shipments, using both its private trucking fleet and for-hire truckers. The costs of the private trucking operations are computed in detail, utilizing data from the firm's files. The relative advantage of the private trucking operation over the best for-hire alternative is used as a measure of the profitability of the private truck operation.

These studies were supported by financial contributions from private firms in the transportation industries, interested shippers in the manufacturing industries, and an interested labor union. Financial support by these organizations does not mean, of course, that they necessarily concur in the results of the study, nor has their financial support in any way influenced its results. A list of the contributing organizations appears at the end of the preface.

The authors wish to offer their special thanks to Mrs. Barbara Mann of Wm. C. Brown Company Publishers for all of her help.

M. L. Burstein[2]

[2]Professor Burstein's paper was prepared while he was with Northwestern University and associated with the Transportation Center. He is now visiting Professor of Economics at the University of Birmingham.

A. Victor Cabot[3]

[3]Northwestern University, Department of Industrial Engineering and Management Sciences and the Transportation Center.

John Egan[4]

[4]University of Chicago, Department of Economics.

Arthur P. Hurter, Jr.[5]

[5]Northwestern University, Department of Industrial Engineering and Management Sciences and the Transportation Center.

Stanley L. Warner[6]

[6]Professor Warner's paper was prepared while he was with Northwestern University and associated with the Transportation Center. He is now with the Department of Economics, Claremont Graduate School.

Acknowledgments

Contributing Organizations:
  Associated Truck Lines, Inc.
  Atlantic Coast Line Railroad Company
  Chesebrough-Pond's, Inc.
  Chicago and North Western Railway Company
  Chicago, Milwaukee, St. Paul and Pacific Railroad Company
  Consolidated Freightways
  Denver & Rio Grande Western Railroad Company
  Denver-Chicago Trucking Company, Inc.
  Gateway Transportation Company
  Great Northern Railway Company
  International Brotherhood of Teamsters, Chauffeurs,
      Warehousemen & Helpers of America
  Interstate Motor Freight System
  McLean Trucking Company
  Missouri Pacific Railroad Company
  New York Central System
  Pacific Intermountain Express
  Procter & Gamble Company, The
  Quaker Oats Company, The
  Red Ball Motor Freight, Inc.
  Ryder System, Inc.
  Western Pacific Railroad Company, The
  Wheels, Inc.
  Yellow Transit Freight Lines, Inc.
      and others.

Contents

CONTENTS

Introduction

The cost of trucking is a diverse and complex topic indeed. One of the problems faced in its study is that the word cost will mean different things to different people. To the highway engineer, the cost of trucking may be associated with highway congestion and roadbed deterioration. To the operator of other modes of transportation, the costs may be measured in terms of traffic diverted away from them to truckers. To the economist interested in the production relationships of the trucking industry, the cost of trucking may be represented by some relationship based on aggregative industry data. To the truck operator, the cost of his trucking operation is related to his own scheduling problem and to the rate of return he can earn on his investment. In this volume, only the cost of trucking from the point of view of the economist looking at the industry as a whole and from the point of view of a truck operator (private or for hire) looking at his operations are considered in the three papers included.

The first paper, by Stanley L. Warner, is concerned with the question of the extent to which larger trucking firms have lower average costs than smaller trucking firms. This question bears importantly on public policy regarding mergers and combinations within the trucking industry. Because of its importance, a number of investigators have examined the problem of relating cost to firm size in this industry. In general they have concluded that if there are any cost savings attributable to size, such savings are apt to be small in percentage terms.

INTRODUCTION

Since profit margins are also small, however, cost advantages which are small in percentage terms may still effect substantial improvements in profitability and competitive position. Warner's paper attempts to estimate the relationship between costs and firm size to a degree precise enough to suggest the order of magnitude as well as the presence or absence of economies of firm size.

The study is built upon the most familiar and conventional estimation approach—that of single equation least squares. This approach is subsequently modified to take account of the peculiarities of cost function estimation. The common carrier nature of the industry suggests the use of a single equation approach since the output side of the cost equation is essentially predetermined. The use of least squares regressions is suggested simply by their success in related studies. The modifications of the usual least squares models that were employed include certain restrictions on the formulation and interpretation of least squares cost functions and the adjustment of certain key estimates for bias due to measurement errors in the variables. The method employed to correct for measurement error bias makes use of replicated observations and is related to the work of Tukey and Madansky.[1]

The particular empirical model adopted for trucking costs specifies total cost as the dependent variable with number of shipments, average length of haul, and average shipment weight as the explanatory variables. The estimation procedure employs yearly data of a cross section of common carrier trucking firms selected in order to avoid firms with interlocking ownerships. After making the adjustments to correct for error bias the estimated basic cost model suggests that—other things being allowed for—a doubling of output is associated with a one to three per cent decline in average costs. A by product of the estimation procedure is the suggestion of a simple rule of thumb measure of trucking output that is much closer to the concept of economic output than is the familiar ton-mile measure.

Following the examination of the relation between average total trucking costs and output, several supplementary investigations are

---

[1]Tukey, J. W., "Components in Regression," *Biometrics*, 7 (1951), 33-70.
Madansky, Albert, "The Fitting of Straight Lines When Both Variables Are Subject to Error," *Journal of the American Statistical Association*, 54 (1959), 173-205.

made to examine their consistency with the basic estimates. The first such supplementary investigation relates the various components of trucking cost to output. A second investigation explores the relation between operating ratios and output, and a third investigation compares changes in scale of individual firms with changes in profitability. All three supplementary investigations are found to be generally consistent with the basic findings.

The conclusions drawn from this investigation may be summarized in the following manner. In terms of theoretical cost models in general the existence of certain "short run" phenomena was shown to bias the cost estimates and to yield difficulties of interpretation. A way of interpreting the "error" term in the cost model allows one to understand the influence of the "short run" phenomena. These phenomena may be thought of as factors preventing firms from attaining long run equilibrium. They consequently distort the observed data which is being used to fit long run cost functions.

The main methodological innovation is the method developed for correcting measurement errors in the independent variable of a regression relationship. The method allowed consistent estimates to be derived for the variance of those measurement errors and for the coefficient relating the true independent and dependent variables. The method proved remarkably simple to apply and interpret.

In applying the cost model to the empirical data, the number of shipments, average shipment weight, and average distance per shipment yielded a rather complete explanation of the costs of the firms in the sample. Ignoring economies of scale for the moment, the estimated relationship for total cost was found:

$$C = A(S) \ (W)^{0.7} \ (T)^{0.3}$$

where   C is total cost, S is the number of shipments, W is the average shipment weight in tons, T is the average mileage per ton and A is a constant of proportionality which depends on the year.

Thus, a 10 per cent increase in average shipment weight is associated with a 7 per cent change in average shipping cost. A 10 per cent change in average haul is associated with a 3 per cent change in average shipping cost. The dependence of total revenue upon output was found to follow much the same pattern, but the difference between the cost and revenue functions was such as to suggest that the heavier and longer haul shipments would be the more profitable ones.

While it is admitted that a different approach might have led to different conclusions, the results obtained clearly suggest the existence of economies of scale. The *smallest* estimate of the scale economies suggests that operating ratios (i.e., the ratio of costs to revenues) should decline by about .01 for a doubling of output. There is no doubt that these economies of large size are of such magnitude that they can be overcome by a favorably situated small firm. The essential determinant of profit in the trucking business is the nature of the collection of shipments made by the firm. A fortuitous enough set of shipments would probably allow even a single truck operator to compete.

On the other hand, the study does suggest that any *given* physical set of shipments can be carried with less cost by a single large firm than by several smaller firms. At least for the size of firms represented by the sample ($1,200,000 average total assets in 1959, average revenue $3,000,000 annually; all are class 1 carriers), there appear to be some natural forces working for combinations and mergers.

The second paper in the volume, that by A. Victor Cabot and Arthur P. Hurter, Jr., is concerned with the development of analytical techniques for the solution of transportation equipment scheduling problems. In particular, the paper is concerned with models of the private truck operator's scheduling problem and with that of the common carrier truck operator. As Warner's paper has already suggested, the geographical distribution of customers and supplies, the size of each shipment and other features of the shipments to be made are very important determinants of the costs of trucking. The model developed in this paper leads to a cost minimizing schedule for a truck operator and also provides a means of investigating the effects of an altered distribution of shipments or a change in firm size on costs.

The ultimate scheduling model is developed gradually, beginning with a relatively simple one period model. Suppose that a private truck operator knows the demands on his firm on a Friday night. These demands are such that they must all be satisfied by the following Friday night. On Monday morning, the scheduler is faced with a certain geographic distribution of his vehicle fleet, left over from the previous week. In addition, he has fixed supplies of the various products of his firm at geographically distributed warehouses. Finally, he knows how much it costs to send a vehicle from any point in the system to any other. Since it is usually desirable to have early rather than late deliveries, if for no reason other than to save storage costs, the costs of shipping from point to point are assumed to be lower earlier in the scheduling week than they are later.

The problem for the scheduler is to schedule his fleet over the week in order to satisfy all the demands for his firm's goods by Friday night, while not exceeding the supplies of any of his warehouses or the capacity of his vehicle fleet, at a minimum cost. A linear programming model was developed to determine the optimal schedule and a sample problem was worked and the results presented. It is, of course, not necessary to consider a scheduling period of one week. Any length of time can be considered in the basic model.

The dual linear programming problem provides a means of determining the effect on the costs of the entire schedule of an additional available vehicle, an increased supply at some particular warehouse or a reduction in some particular demand. The dual variables thus afford a means of determining what the firm should be willing to pay for the use of an additional vehicle (i.e., the maximum rental it should pay for an additional vehicle) or an additional unit of warehouse capacity. The dual variables furthermore provide a means of determining whether an additional unit of demand will or will not add more to revenues than to costs. Here the costs are not only the direct costs of making the additional shipment but also those associated with the alternative uses of the limited number of vehicles and supplies.

The second section of this paper develops an analagous one period model for the common carrier. In this case, each shipment must be identified. A common carrier does not have the option of routing commodity shipments in order to minimize costs. He must deliver particular packages from specified origins to specified destinations. In so doing, he can minimize costs only over the scheduling of his vehicle fleet. Again a linear programming model was developed and the results of a sample problem presented. In this case, the dual variables may be interpreted as the minimum rates the trucker should charge for his services and again may be valauble for management planning.

INTRODUCTION

Returning to the general problem of the shipper's attempt to minimize his transportation costs, the private carrier model is extended to include the use of common carrier trucking services. Generally speaking, very few firms rely exclusively on their own trucking fleet to meet even a stable, predictable set of demands. There may well be circumstances under which the private fleet is best for some share of a firm's shipments while the use of for-hire carriers is better for others. The model developed in the paper allows a shipment to be made in such a way that the total transportation expense over the whole scheduling period is a minimum regardless of whether private or for-hire carriage is selected (by the model) for that particular shipment.

It is shown that scheduling models accounting for maintenance schedules or driver schedules are apt to become too complex to be computationally useful. The added complexities stem from the necessity of identifying each truck. A formal model is presented using the identity of each truck making each shipment throughout the period as the unknowns.

Throughout the discussion of the single scheduling period models presented thus far, the truck operator has been assumed to be confronted with a given geographic distribution of his vehicle fleet. Clearly, the nature of this initial distribution does much to determine the lower bound on transportation costs that might be achieved during the ensuing period. A fleet operator is therefore ultimately concerned with more than a single scheduling period (e.g., "week"). He realizes that the final vehicle distribution of one period, since it will be the initial vehicle distribution of the next, influences the level of costs that can be attained in the next. The scheduler might attempt to account for this interaction, in a single period model, by specifying the final distribution of trucks in each scheduling period. Several alternatives are suggested and investigated using numerical examples.

A natural extension of the work on initial vehicle distribution is to include the initial vehicle distribution, for any scheduling period, as a variable in the cost minimization model. The dual linear programming problem yields a variable which can be interpreted as the value of the entire vehicle fleet to the shipper, given the shipper's demands and warehouse supplies. The optimal initial distribution is determined for a numerical example and the minimum level of costs attained compared with those attained in other examples.

The effect of firm size on its average shipping costs was investigated through the use of numerical examples. In one case, the shipping problem of a large firm was divided exactly in half with no effect on average cost. In another case, the total to be shipped and the vehicle fleet of a large firm were divided among two smaller firms so that the totals were again equal. This time, however, instead of dividing each demand, each supply, and each initial regional distribution of vehicles in half as before, certain demands, supplies and vehicles were assigned to each of the two smaller firms. In other words, although each small firm had one-half of the total demands, supplies and vehicles of the larger firm, the geographic distribution of these quantities differed. In this case, the total shipping costs of the two smaller firms exceeded that of the larger firm. Thus, if some form of geographic complementarity exists between the shipping patterns of two smaller firms, their combined shipping costs can be reduced through a merger. These results are entirely consistent with those of Warner.

The final step in the development of a comprehensive scheduling model for trucking consists of extending the planning horizon of the firm beyond one scheduling period. Suppose that the scheduling period we have been dealing with can be thought of as one week. Consider a firm that wants to schedule its shipments for one month in advance. Although the shipper is still faced with weekly demands, he knows these demands for one month in advance. There are many reasons why the firm might wish to undertake such a multi-period scheduling problem. First, it will tell him the allocation of his trucks in advance so that he can better schedule his drivers. Second, if he knows the route his trucks are to take for this longer period, he will be better able to consider maintenance problems. Third, scheduling over several scheduling periods allows the firm to take into account the relationships between the minimum cost attainable for a period and the initial distribution of vehicles for that period (i.e., the final distribution of the previous period).

This extension of the problem makes it very large from a computational point of view. Consequently, straightforward computations based on the usual linear programming techniques are infeasible except for problems with very few regions and only a few "weeks" in the "month" long scheduling horizon. Two alternative computational techniques are presented in detail. One is based on the concept of dynamic programming and the other on the decomposition principle of linear programming.

Warner's paper dealt with trucking costs using aggregative statistics for relatively large trucking firms. Cabot and Hurter dealt with a particular and important aspect of trucking costs not captured in aggregative statistics, the scheduling problem. While the method developed is thought to be applicable to any firm contemplating private truck operations, no direct application was attempted. Although the scheduling aspects of the problem are important, they are by no means the only important aspects of the shipping problem. The paper by Burstein and Egan attempts to analyse the over-all problem of the efficient use of private trucking by a firm through the presentation of a detailed case study. Case studies are, of course, very important contributors to the development of general methods of analysis. In particular, they help to establish the relative importance of various aspects of a problem when it is not *a priori* obvious.

Burstein and Egan attempt to answer the question: Why should firms operate private motor carriage? Making the implicit assumption of a profit maximizing motivation for the firm they are able to answer the question with: In order to save money. This leads directly to another question: Why should firms be able to save money by doing for themselves what professionals are willing to do for them? It is this question which serves to give direction to the study. The question leads to the following testable hypothesis: Even in elemental haulage where special-service considerations may be ignored, freight rates determined by official fiat are likely to reflect costs so badly that public carriers are forced to quote "inaccurate" tariffs. Professionals are forced to behave like rank amateurs.

This hypothesis proved relatively easy to test (partially), because the experience of a large wholesale grocer, who operated nationwide private carriage, was available. Using data obtained from piecemeal study of the firm's operations, shipping activities were broken down into component parts: loading, hauling (including fuel and labor inputs), unloading, and the like. Employing standard methods of multiple correlation, estimates were made (with very small standard errors) of what economists call *variable expenses,* roughly speaking, out-of-pocket costs.

Then capital expenses were laboriously, if crudely, computed. In other words, appropriate interest and depreciation charges for regularly recurring hauls between such points as Chicago and San Francisco were calculated. This allowed the construction of basic rates, reflecting capital costs, to which could be added out-of-pocket costs for alternative cargos.

The authors believe that the resulting figures support their hypothesis. The data showed that properly-computed cost differentials, let alone basic costs, differed importantly from those implied in the public-carriage rate structure. The company was encouraged thereby to roll its own. The biases discovered were especially large for long hauls. In addition the work suggests that, if it were not for legal limitations on back-haul, there would be much more private carriage than there actually is.

Finally, the study implies that a competitive trucking industry's tariffs would not be as volatile as some have supposed. It turns out that out-of-pocket expenses loom larger than might be expected. Still the authors are careful to point out that even a competitive and unregulated motor haulage industry would probably not be perfectly *efficient* in the way that economists use that word.

Chapter 1

Cost Models, Measurement Errors, and Economies of Scale In Trucking

Introduction

One conclusion regarding economies of scale in the trucking business is established. If there are economies, there are not many. This conclusion is *a priori* reasonable in view of the nearly perfect divisibilities that characterize the industry. The conclusion has been made more certain by the empirical studies of a number of investigators.[1] The general concensus of these studies is that the variation that exists between the costs of large and small firms is explained primarily by such considerations as length of haul.[2] There are not many differences left to be explained by scale itself.

In the trucking industry, however, operating margins are very small. Even minute changes in cost effect substantial changes in profitability and competitive position.[3] It is therefore of interest to continue the investigation to discover whether there are any economies at all, and to seek to quantify the answer. The empirical part of this study is directed toward that end.

The other part of the study is concerned with general cost function and least squares methodology—particularly as applied to investigations of economies of scale. The main results of this section are a development of the cost model and a statistically consistent method for

[1]Department of Economics, Claremont Graduate School, Claremont, California and formerly at the Transportation Center at Northwestern University.

1

handling measurement errors in least squares estimations. The remarks on the cost model should generally be appropriate for other industries besides the trucking industry. The remarks concerning errors in variables should generally be appropriate for estimations besides those of cost functions.

1.1 LINEAR COST FUNCTIONS AND LEAST SQUARES ESTIMATION

Investigating economies of scale involves estimating the relation between cost and output. This, in turn, involves the choice of a cost estimation procedure. In this study it was decided to begin with the most conventional estimation procedure—that associated with the estimation of linear models through least squares criteria. This method historically has been applied in countless cost studies. More recently it provided the central method for a whole book of cost studies by a leading econometrician.[4] Least squares analysis is accordingly the departure point for the present study. The standard least squares cost models are reviewed and discussed; then certain modifications are suggested in an effort to better adapt conventional procedures for cost function estimation. The empirical part of the study is in part an application of these results to the problem of exploring economies of scale in the trucking industry.

In its most basic form the conventional linear cost model takes one of the following expressions:

$$(1) \qquad C_t = a + b\, O_t + u_t$$

$$(2) \qquad \log C_t = a + b \log O_t + u_t \,.$$

In each case C_t and O_t represent the observed total cost and output of observation t. The symbol u_t represents a random disturbance for observation t that satisfies $E(u_t) = 0$, $E(u_t O_t) = 0$, and $E(u_t u_k) = \sigma^2$ or 0 according as t is or is not equal to k.

The estimated cost function is conventionally identified as a "long run" or "short run" function according to whether the observations are drawn from a cross section of firms or a time series of the same firm. In the non-logarithmic formulation the presence of economies of scale is inferred by the estimate of an "a" which is significantly

2

greater than 0. This is done since such a function implies that average cost falls with increasing output. In the logarithmic formulation the presence of economies of scale is inferred instead by an estimate of "b" which is significantly less than 1. That is, in the logarithmic formulation, an estimate of "b" less than 1 describes a cost function in which costs increase less than in proportion to output.

Concern with economies of scale implies concern with the long run cost functions rather than short run cost functions. Since it has already been noted that the basic cost model sometimes refers to one concept and sometimes to the other concept, it is important to have in mind a consistent model that accounts for the difference. As it stands, the basic cost model is clearly subject to certain paradoxes. For example, suppose the model

$$C_{tj} = a + b \, O_{tj} + u_{tj} \qquad j = 1, 2, \ldots, n$$

is considered as referring to the cost function of a series of n different firms at time t. Then, by convention, the parameter "b" in the true relation is interpreted as a long run cost parameter. The cost function of the same firms in the period t-1 could be described as

$$C_{t-1,j} = a + b \, O_{t-1,j} + u_{t-1,j} \qquad j = 1, 2, \ldots, n.$$

Again b is interpreted as the long run cost coefficient. But subtracting this equation from the previous one shows

$$(C_{t_j} - C_{t-1._j}) = b \, (O_{t_j} - O_{t-1._j}) + (u_{t_j} - u_{t-1,_j}).$$

Mathematically this b is the same b as in the other two equations, and this implies that its interpretation should be the same. But probably most observers would prefer to interpret this estimate as reflecting short run phenomena. That is, it can be argued that the time change from t-1 to t is insufficient for a full adjustment of all variable factors so that the b estimated in this relation is more like a short run parameter. Thus there is a paradox in that mathematics and economics disagree on how this b should be interpreted.

A simple device which can be used to account for this and other paradoxes is provided by slightly altering the basic models (1) and (2) to

(3) $$C_t = a + b \, O_t + S_t + e_t , \text{ and}$$

(4) $$\log C_t = a + b \log O_t + \log P_t + e_t.$$

In the non-logarithmic version, S_t is interpreted as the amount of total cost that is due to lack of full adjustment of costs to output. This variable thus stands for an added amount of cost due to short run effects. In the logarithmic version, P_t is interpreted as a scale factor which multiplies "fully adjusted cost" by some number $\geqq 1$ to bring it to total cost. The logarithm of P_t is thus an added amount which also reflects short run effects. In both cases the term e_t is interpreted as reflecting various unsystematic influences and may be expected to vary from firm to firm and from time to time. The same least squares properties are assigned to e_t as were previously assigned to u_t.

Naturally the variables S_t and P_t will ordinarily not be observable quantities, and they cannot be specifically introduced into an estimating equation. But merely recognizing the character of these effects suggests a more organized approach to the natural appropriateness of different cost functions. In particular, this simple amendment suggests certain propositions bearing on least squares estimation of any linear cost model. Supposing that the assumed cost model is of the type illustrated by equations (1) and (2), the following statements are made.

I. There is a theoretical asymmetry in the distribution of errors which is apt to prevail about the true cost function. In particular, the standard least squares assumption that $E(u_t) = 0$ is not likely to be satisfied.

II. The least squares estimate of the constant term is biased upward in both the regular and the logarithmic formulations of the linear model. In addition, the output coefficient will tend to be biased in the regular formulation.

III. Cross section estimates of cost functions should not rely on data from a single year.

IV. The interpretative paradox between cross section and first difference regressions can be accounted for by the omitted short run term.

Statement I comes from recognizing the presence of two different components in the random term appropriate for cost analysis. To begin with, assuming the model to be $C_t = a + b\,O_t + u_t$, or log $C_t = a + b$ log $O_t + u_t$, the implication of (3) and (4) is that $u_t = S_t + e_t$ or $u_t =$ log $P_t + e_t$ respectively. Thus the assumed

4

u_t in either case is the sum of a short run component and an error term. The character of the short run component is a result of the definition of long run cost. That is, economic theory defines long run cost for a given output as minimum attainable cost for that output. Thus, if $a + b\,O_t$ is a true long run cost function and an observation is made of a cross section of firms each of whose costs follow this function, economic theory would suggest that the only attainable departures from this function would all have to be positive. The observed costs might exceed the long run costs because of short run phenomena, but the observed costs could not fall below the long run costs. At the very least this would suggest that the components called S_t and $\log P_t$ would take on only positive values. In the extreme case in which the economic definitions of cost and output applied exactly, the component called e_t could be considered identically equal to 0, and the relevant error term for estimation would itself take on only positive values.

More generally, it is reasonable in any empirical work to expect to encounter disturbances due to e_t as well as S_t and $\log P_t$. Accounting costs differ from the pure concepts defined by economic theory. Moreover, there are accounting and production function differences among different firms and even for the same firm at different time periods. Thus the empirical notion of a long run cost curve must additionally allow for e_t, an unsystematic measurement difference between the true and observed cost figures. The distribution of this error component of the disturbance term could be expected to be symmetrical with mean 0.

The remarks on the composition of the u_t term in (1) and (2) may therefore be summarized as follows. In part this term should reflect short run cost disturbances which are positive deviations from the true function. In part this term should reflect the possibility of errors of measurement in costs and other random influences. Since as a first approximation the distribution of the measurement part ought to be symmetric with mean 0, the net result of the two influences should still be a disturbance whose distribution involves an expected value greater than 0. This is statement I.

Most of statement II is the result of simply deriving the theoretical least squares estimates of "a" and "b" under the assumption that

$E(u_t) = k \neq 0$. The result is that the assumption $E(u_t) \neq 0$ results in a bias in the estimate of "a" but not in the estimate of "b."

To develop the rest of the second statement, note that in the non-logarithmic formulation it is likely that the S_t of a given year will tend to be relatively large for those observations in which O_t is large. That is, as a first approximation, it might be supposed that $S_t = k\,O_t$, the short run impact being exactly proportional to total output. More generally, even if different firms had different k's for a given year, the firms with larger outputs could be expected on average to at least have absolutely larger short run effects. Thus O_t and S_t should be correlated, and therefore O_t is correlated with u_t which contains S_t. This violates the chief least squares assumption $E(u_t\,O_t) = 0$. Therefore the estimate of b in the non-logarithmic formulation has virtually no properties. In particular it is biased.

On the other hand, in the logarithmic formulation, $\log P_t$ is the log of a scale factor and is therefore less likely to be related to O_t. That is, while the absolute effect of short run disturbances is surely greater for larger firms, it is not so obvious that there should be any close relation between size of firm and the proportionality factors themselves. Consequently, in the logarithmic case, u_t is not so apt to be correlated with $\log O_t$. Therefore the estimate of b in this relation is apt to be less biased.

It is worth noting that the arguments of this section tend to support the logarithmic formulation of the cost model for an investigation of economies of scale. This follows from the fact that the constant term tends to be biased upward in both formulations. In the logarithmic formulation this particular estimate is of secondary interest anyway. But in the non-logarithmic formulation it is this estimate that is used to infer the presence or absence of economies of scale. If the non-logarithmic formulation is used, the results will therefore tend to over-emphasize the economies of scale.

Statement III is a result of the discussion of the first two propositions. In any given year there are short run effects that are compounded in with the error term. The previous discussion has indicated that this may not be innocuous—particularly for the non-logarithmic form—but more generally it is true regardless of the formulation. This would suggest that the short run effects of any given year might impart a special bias to the estimations. Deriving estimates for several different years should help offset this type of interference.

The last of the four statements is intended as a representative statement of the fact that most theoretical cost function phenomena are interpretable within this quite simple model. The comparison between regular cross section regression and the cross section regression of first differences can be taken as an example.

To fix on a specific form of the model suppose that the relation refers to logarithms, i.e., that the true model is

$$(5) \qquad \log C_t = a + b \log O_t + u_t \text{ where}$$
$$u_t = \log P_t + e_t .$$

As before, the usual assumptions are posited for e_t. In addition suppose that $u_t = \log P_t + e_t$ is uncorrelated with $\log O_t$. Then note that if (5) is used for a cross section regression the estimate of "a" will be biased since $E(u_t) = E(\log P_t)$, but "b" will not be biased and is interpretable as a long run cost parameter.

Now consider the relation

$$(6) \qquad (\log C_t - \log C_{t-1}) = b(\log O_t - \log O_{t-1}) + (u_t - u_{t-1}) .$$

The error term in this expression is

$$(7) \qquad (u_t - u_{t-1}) = \log P_t - \log P_{t-1} + e_t - e_{t-1}.$$

It may first be noted that

$$E(u_t - u_{t-1}) = E(\log P_t - \log P_{t-1})$$

which will be 0 only by accident. Even more important is the fact that there are now again persuasive reasons why the error term $(u_t - u_{t-1})$ should be correlated with $(\log O_t - \log O_{t-1})$. This is because $(\log P_t - \log P_{t-1})$ reflects the change in the relation between short run costs and total costs for the two periods. On average it is to be expected that the impact of extra short run costs should be related to temporary, unexpected, or unplanned changes in output. These output changes would be included in the observed output changes. Thus the output variable would be correlated with the $(u_t - u_{t-1})$ variable, and this in turn would dictate that the coefficient of the output variable should be interpreted as something other than the long run coefficient. Under certain circumstances it might be possible to identify this estimate with a particular short run relationship.

7

In the model just outlined, it is possible to think of the time gap as pertaining to an arbitrary number of years. In this context it is important to make the following note for later use. The longer the time gap involved between t and t-1, the less likely it is that the observable output changes are dominated by temporary, unexpected, or unplanned changes. Thus the longer the time gap involved in the first difference formulation, the more reasonable it is to assume that the estimate of b still refers to the long run coefficient. (In a sense the regular cross section regression is just a limiting form of the first difference regression.) What is "long enough" for this result must be decided separately for different industries.

1.2 ERRORS IN VARIABLES AND THE LINEAR COST MODEI

The implications of the basic cost model have been described. It remains to explore certain extensions that are relevant for particular empirical applications. The usual extensions that are incorporated include the addition of more variables and possibly more equations. More variables are added so that the notion of output can be considered more nearly homogeneous from firm to firm and time to time. More equations are added principally to avoid simultaneity bias. One other complication, however, is difficult to avoid. This concerns the possible errors that are incorporated into the variable identified with observed output.

The remarks in a previous paragraph pointed out the general inappropriateness of assuming the cost variable to be an errorless approximation of actual economic cost. The same comments can be made concerning the relation between observed reported output and the notion of output dealt with in economic theory. No matter what variable is observed as a proxy variable for economic output, only under exceptional circumstances could it be regarded as the "errorless" measurement of economic output. Reasons for this are straightforward. At different time periods the same firm will have quality variations and changes in service that might well not appear in any index of reported output. Explicitly considering more features of the product might reduce this error. It would not eliminate it. These same comments, of course, apply to different firms with ostensibly the same cost function observed at one point in time.

It is true that such errors are often ignored, and a reasonable question might ask why the estimated relation cannot be portrayed as that between reported cost and reported output. These variables at least could be measured without error. The answer is that such a relation can be estimated, but that it cannot be interpreted in the same way as the economic model. That is, the parameters a and b that relate reported output to reported cost would not signify economies of scale (or their absence) in the same way that the parameters a and b of the theoretical relation do. In particular, if the relation between reported figures is used, it can be shown that under the usual assumptions regarding error distributions the a and b estimates would tend to overstate the case for economies of scale. The conclusion is an application of familiar results concerning least squares estimates when there are measurement errors in the variables. The results are as follows:

Let $c = a' + b'o + e$ where c and o are the true economic variables. Suppose that $C = c + g$ and $O = o + f$ are the variables which are observed and which are taken as proxy variables for c and o. Now suppose g and f are random variables with expectation 0 and variance $\sigma^2(g)$ and $\sigma^2(f)$ respectively; g, f, and e are independent of o and each other; and g and f are independent of c. Then

$$(8) \qquad \text{plim } \hat{b} = b'\left[\frac{1}{1 + \dfrac{\sigma^2(f)}{\sigma^2(o)}}\right]$$

where $\hat{b}$ is the estimate secured from estimating the relation $C = a + bO + u$ by ordinary least squares. The symbol $\sigma^2(o)$ stands for the limiting value of the sampling variance of the unobservable true independent variable. Thus if $\hat{b}$ is regarded as an estimate of b', the true parameter, then the estimate consistently tends to be too small by a factor of

$$\left[\frac{1}{1 + \dfrac{\sigma^2(f)}{\sigma^2(o)}}\right]^5.$$

9

If â is also regarded as an estimate of a′, the true parameter, then â will also be an estimate that tends to be too high. Letting $\overline{C}$ and $\overline{O}$ stand for the sample means, this can be seen as follows:

$$\text{Plim } \hat{a} = \text{Plim } (\overline{C} - \hat{b}\overline{O})$$

$$= E(\overline{C}) - \text{Plim } \hat{b} \ (E(\overline{O}))$$

$$= E(\overline{C}) - (\frac{1}{1 + \dfrac{\sigma^2 \ (f)}{\sigma^2 \ (o)}}) \ b' \ E(\overline{O})$$

$$> E(\overline{C}) - b'E(\overline{O}) = a'$$

since b′ is positive. Thus the effect of errors in the output variable serves to overstate economies of scale no matter which formulation is used. The fact that $\hat{b}$ is estimated too small gives this result for the logarithmic formulation. The fact that â is estimated too big gives the result for the non-logarithmic formulation.

The errors in the output variable can be ignored or an attempt can be made to incorporate them into the analysis. If the errors in the output variable are ignored there is the question of whether or not the bias is apt to be serious. It is clear from equation (8) that the bias in the estimated parameter depends on the ratio of the variance of the output error to the limiting form of the sample variance of the true output. For example, the relation shows that if the ratio of the two key variances were .1, the parameter estimate would be biased downward by about 10 per cent. Similarly if the key ratio were .5, so that the variance of the observable independent variable is about ⅔ due to variance in true output and ⅓ due to measurement error, the parameter estimate would be biased downward by about 33 per cent. Unfortunately, it is not generally easy to estimate the error variance. Beyond certain subjective suppositions, the researcher is usually in the dark concerning this type of bias.

Methods for handling measurement error include bounding methods[6], grouping methods[7], instrumental variable methods[8], and actual estimation of error variance through Tintner's Variate Difference Method[9]. All these methods are time-consuming, and some have the disadvantage of a certain amount of arbitrariness in their application. In this study it is suggested that a consistent estimate of the error variance can be quite simply derived through the use of regular cross section regression combined with cross section regression of certain first differences. Since the estimate is statistically consistent, it also allows a statistically consistent method for correcting the parameter estimates for the effect of measurement errors.

For a heuristic form of the estimation method it may be supposed that the true relation

$$(9) \qquad c_{tj} = a' + b'o_{tj} + e_{tj}$$

is to be estimated essentially by cross section observations $j = 1$ to n taken at time t. The observed variables are

$$C_{tj} = c_{tj} + g_{tj} \text{ and}$$
$$O_{tj} = o_{tj} + f_{tj}.$$

The assumptions already given for the standard error model are presumed to apply. The additional assumptions made here involve the extension of the same assumptions to cover a first difference form of the same regression. Namely, the error model assumptions already listed are supposed good for both the time periods t and p involved in the first difference regression. In addition, the measurement errors at different time periods are assumed independent and of equal variance between time periods as well as across locations. Finally, all the independence relations postulated between different variables in the same time period are assumed to hold between those variables in the two different time periods.

Writing now the corresponding relations at time p as

$$(10) \qquad c_{pj} = a' + b'o_{pj} + e_{pj} \text{ with}$$
$$C_{pj} = c_{pj} + g_{pj} \text{ and}$$
$$O_{pj} = o_{pj} + f_{pj},$$

the true difference relationship is (9) – (10) which is

$$(11) \qquad (c_{tj} - c_{pj}) = d'(o_{tj} - o_{pj}) + (e_{tj} - e_{pj}) .$$

The derived relationships of observables to unobservables are

$$(C_{tj} - C_{pj}) = (c_{tj} - c_{pj}) + (g_{tj} - g_{pj}) \text{ and}$$
$$(O_{tj} - O_{pj}) = (o_{tj} - o_{pj}) + (f_{tj} - f_{pj}),$$

11

and it is supposed that (t-p) is a long enough time period so that $d' = b'$. By the extended assumptions this first difference form of the relation also satisfies the assumptions of the standard error model.

Now, from equation (8) the statistical statement of bias for the relation at time t is

$$(12) \qquad \text{Plim } \hat{b} = b' \left(\cfrac{1}{1 + \cfrac{\sigma^2 (f_t)}{\sigma^2 (o_t)}} \right).$$

The symbol $\hat{b}$ is the estimate of the coefficient in the relationship between the observed variables C_t and O_t. The symbols $\sigma^2 (f_t)$ and $\sigma^2 (o_t)$ respectively correspond to the variances of the error and true components of the regular cross section regression accomplished for time t.

Similarly, if $\hat{d}$ is the estimate of the coefficient $d' = b'$ accomplished through the regression of first differences,

$$(13) \qquad \text{Plim } \hat{d} = b' \left(\cfrac{1}{1 + \cfrac{\sigma^2 (f_t - f_p)}{\sigma^2 (o_t - o_p)}} \right).$$

Here the symbols $\sigma^2 (f_t - f_p)$ and $\sigma^2 (o_t - o_p)$ respectively correspond to the variances of the error and true components for the first difference regression.

Solving (12) and (13) for b' and equating the resulting expressions shows

$$(14) \quad \left(1 + \frac{\sigma^2 (f_t)}{\sigma^2 (o_t)}\right) \text{Plim } \hat{b} = \left(1 + \frac{\sigma^2 (f_t - f_p)}{\sigma^2 (o_t - o_p)}\right) \text{Plim } \hat{d}.$$

Now recalling that $O_t = o_t + f_t$, and that by hypothesis o_t and f_t are independent, $\sigma^2 (O_t) = \sigma^2 (o_t) + \sigma^2 (f_t)$, where $\sigma^2 (O_t)$ is the variance of the observed variable. Moreover, $\sigma^2 (O_t - O_p) = \sigma^2 (o_t - o_p + f_t - f_p) = \sigma^2 (o_t - o_p) + \sigma^2 (f_t - f_p) = \sigma^2 (o_t - o_p) + 2\sigma^2 (f_t)$ by the independence of $(o_t - o_p)$, f_t, and f_p, and by the fact that $\sigma^2 (f_t) = \sigma^2 (f_p)$. Then substituting for $\sigma^2 (o_t)$, $\sigma^2 (o_t - o_p)$, and $\sigma^2 (f_t - f_p)$ in (14) provides

12

$$(15) \quad \left(1 + \frac{\sigma^2(f_t)}{\sigma^2(O_t) - \sigma^2(f_t)}\right) \text{Plim } \hat{b} = \left(1 + \frac{2\sigma^2(f_t)}{\sigma^2(O_t - O_p) - 2\sigma^2(f_t)}\right) \text{Plim } \hat{d}$$

Thus $\quad [\sigma^2(O_t - O_p) - 2\sigma^2(f_t)] \, [\sigma^2(O_t)] \text{ Plim } \hat{b}$

$$= [\sigma^2(O_t) - \sigma^2(f_t)] \, [\sigma^2(O_t - O_p)] \text{ Plim } \hat{d}$$

and this expression may be solved for $\sigma^2(f_t)$.

The result is

$$(16) \qquad \sigma^2(f_t) = \frac{[\text{Plim } \hat{b} - \text{Plim } \hat{d}] \, [\sigma^2(O_t) \, \sigma^2(O_t - O_p)]}{\text{Plim } \hat{b} \, (2\sigma^2(O_t)) - \text{Plim } \hat{d} \, [\sigma^2(O_t - O_p)]} \, .$$

Now let the sample variance of $(O_t - O_p)$ be $\hat{\sigma}^2(O_t - O_p)$, the sample variance of O_t be $\hat{\sigma}^2(O_t)$, and define an estimate of $\sigma^2(f_t)$ as

$$(17) \qquad \hat{\sigma}^2(f_t) = \frac{[\hat{b} - \hat{d}] \, [\hat{\sigma}^2(O_t - O_p) \, \hat{\sigma}^2(O_t)]}{\hat{b} \, [2\hat{\sigma}^2(O_t)] - \hat{d} \, [\hat{\sigma}^2(O_t - O_p)]} \, .$$

Then note from (15) and (16) that $\hat{\sigma}^2(f_t)$ is clearly a consistent estimate of $\sigma^2(f_t)$; i.e., Plim $\hat{\sigma}^2(f_t) = \sigma^2(f_t)$. Finally define the estimates

$$(18) \qquad \text{adj } \hat{b} = \hat{b} \left[1 + \frac{\hat{\sigma}^2(f_t)}{\hat{\sigma}^2(O_t) - \hat{\sigma}^2(f_t)}\right], \text{ and}$$

$$(19) \qquad \text{adj } \hat{d} = \hat{d} \left[1 + \frac{2\hat{\sigma}^2(f_t)}{\hat{\sigma}^2(O_t - O_p) - 2\hat{\sigma}^2(f_t)}\right] .$$

Taking probability limits of (18) shows [using (12) and the relations following (14)]

$$(20) \quad \text{Plim (adj } \hat{b}) = \text{Plim } \hat{b} \left[1 + \frac{\text{Plim } \hat{\sigma}^2(f_t)}{\text{Plim } \hat{\sigma}^2(O_t) - \text{Plim } \hat{\sigma}^2(f_t)}\right]$$

$$= b' \left[\frac{1}{1 + \frac{\sigma^2(f_t)}{\sigma^2(O_t)}}\right] \left[1 + \frac{\sigma^2(f_t)}{\sigma^2(O_t) - \sigma^2(f_t)}\right]$$

$$= b' \, .$$

Similarly from (19) [using (13) and the relations following (14)]

$$(21) \text{ Plim (adj } \hat{d}) = \text{Plim } \hat{d} \left[1 + \frac{2 \text{ Plim } \hat{\sigma}^2 (f_t)}{\text{Plim } \hat{\sigma}^2 (O_t - O_p) - 2 \text{ Plim } \hat{\sigma}^2 (f_t)}\right]$$

$$= b' \left[\frac{1}{1 + \dfrac{\sigma^2 (f_t - f_p)}{\sigma^2 (o_t - o_p)}}\right] \left[1 + \frac{2\sigma^2 (f_t)}{\sigma^2 (O_t - O_p) - 2\sigma^2 (f_t)}\right]$$

$$= b' .$$

Both adj $\hat{b}$ and adj $\hat{d}$ are therefore consistent estimates of the true parameter. Thus to compute an estimate of b', use (17) to secure the estimate of the error variance and then substitute in either (18) or (19). Both substitutions provide the same estimate of b'.[10] Note especially that a consistent estimate of the true parameter can therefore be computed using only the ordinary least squares estimates $\hat{b}$ and $\hat{d}$ together with the sample variances of the observable variables O_t and $(O_t - O_p)$. Since these sample variances are computational by-products of the regular least squares estimates of $\hat{b}$ and $\hat{d}$, the consistent estimate of the true parameter b' is easily calculated.

1.3 COSTS AND ECONOMIES OF SCALE IN THE TRUCKING INDUSTRY

The main determinants of differences in average costs among trucking firms are the various characteristics of their shipments. Certain physical characteristics of individual shipments are important, such as shape and weight, and certain characteristics of the aggregate collection are important, such as the distribution of shipment origins and destinations. Since such considerations as these are the main determinants of average costs, it is possible for small or even single truck operations to attain low costs if they are presented with a favorable enough collection of shipments. The question as to whether or not there are economies of scale in the trucking business thus makes sense only in terms of *given* collections of shipments. Is size an advantage in the servicing of given collections of shipments? Stated another way, given two collections of shipments, would a single organization be expected to carry the combined collections more cheaply than two separate organizations? Or finally, supposing the character of the shipments to remain essentially the same, do the scheduling and consolidating advantages of a greater number of shipments outweigh the traditional coordination difficulties associated with larger firm size?

The statistical problem in examining for such economies of scale centers around the difficult practical problem of distinguishing which differences in observed costs are attributable to output differences and which to mere product differences. An added complication is provided by the already observed fact that the cost differences of interest are apt to be very small. Taken together, these two considerations suggest that empirical conclusions regarding economies of scale in the trucking industry may be somewhat sensitive to the method employed for the investigation.

1.4 ESTIMATION MODEL FOR TRUCKING COSTS

The starting place for the development of a particular cost model for trucking is the identification of a variable associated with output and a variable associated with cost of output.

To take the output variable first, it is clear that if all shipments were alike, there would be no difficulty in the choice of an output variable. The variable "number of shipments" would itself be a natural measure of output. A firm whose shipments were twice those of another would clearly have twice the output of the other. However, shipments differ. The differences concern weight, size, length of trip, and ease of pickup and delivery—to name only a few considerations. Since ideally an output measure should reflect all such considerations, an absolutely true measure of output for a firm over a given time period could only be a list of all the individual shipments made.

Such a list is not ordinarily available and it would be a cumbersome set of statistics if it were. What are available are some aggregated summary measures which at least partially reflect the composition of an individual firm's shipments over a given period of time. Average weight per shipment (total tons/number of shipments) and average haul (total ton miles/total tons)[11] are two such measures that appear of obvious importance. These features are clearly important as cost affecting properties of individual shipments. By presumption they are also important as cost affecting properties of an aggregated number of individual shipments.

Considerations of haul and weight obviously don't summarize all the properties of the aggregated number of shipments. For example, the questions of average shape and dimension are not necessarily covered. Another omitted factor concerns the question of how separated in space is the collection of shipment origins and destinations. Finally, the dimension concerning speed of trip is overlooked.

The haul and weight variables, however, besides being easier to measure, do have the virtue of appearing to be the two most important variables. They are the ones which obviously are suggested by the physics of the problem. Work is done by moving a given weight over a given distance. If the speed of all truck trips is roughly the same, the physical effort required in a given period depends mainly upon the weight and the distance. Thus the following statement seems reasonable. *If two firms have the same average weight per shipment and the same average haul, the firm with the greater number of shipments is ordinarily the firm with the larger output.* The statement is even more appealing when considering the same firm at two different points in time. Accordingly, it is this statement that forms the central basis for the cost model. The model then asserts total cost to be a function of the total number of shipments, the average weight per shipment, the length of haul, and a random factor. In symbols, $C = f(O,W,H,U)$ where the letter represention of the variables is obvious.[12] For this study, the functional relation is presumed to be of the form

$$C = b_0 O^{b_2} \ W^{b_3} \ H^{b_4} \ (10)^U.$$

Thus $\log C = b_1 + b_2 \log O + b_3 \log W + b_4 \log H + U$, one of the forms typically selected for cost functions.

The choice of the logarithmic form is partly arbitrary. In part, however, the choice for this study is motivated by certain considerations. First, in the logarithmic formulation, evidence regarding economies of scale is provided by parameter estimates other than those of the constant term. The constant was shown to be subject to special bias in cost function estimation. Second, the logarithmic form appears better adapted to the errors in variable model developed in the last section. In the logarithmic formulation of the cost model, the additive form of the output variable error term corresponds to a statement of proportionality between the true output and the observed output. The log of the proportionality factor plays the part of the unknown random error. The assumption of independence between the true output component and the error component would thus seem easier to justify in this case than in the case where the true output component and its error were measured naturally. Third, the logarithmic formulation is suggested by the standard physics model expressing work done in overcoming friction. That is, considering a single shipment, the force needed to overcome friction is proportional to weight, and work depends upon a multiplicative relation between force and distance. As a first approximation, cost should be proportional to work, so a micro model for a single shipment might be $C = b_0 WH$. This last expression is included in $C = b_0 O^{b_2} W^{b_3} H^{b_4}$, the functional form assumed for study.[13]

One final advantage of the logarithmic form is that of interpretative convenience. Recalling that H was defined as (ton miles/tons) and W as (tons/shipments), the model can be written as

$$C = b_0 \text{ (shipments)}^{b_2} \text{ (tons/shipments)}^{b_3} \text{ (ton miles/tons)}^{b_4} \quad (10).^{v}$$

In this form it can be seen that the model is essentially a generalization of the familiar notion identifying output with ton miles. That is, if b_2, b_3, and b_4 were all estimated to be 1, the product of the three right-hand factors would reduce to simple ton miles. The fact that the estimated parameters can differ from 1 and from each other thus creates a competing index to ton miles. The competing index allows for different effects upon costs depending on whether reported ton miles were generated by longer haul, greater weight, or simply more shipments.

1.5 ESTIMATION OF THE MODEL

The primary estimation method for the study involved a cross section analysis of present day trucking firms which were classified as carriers of general freight. The data used consisted exclusively of individual firm reports collected and published by Trinc Associates, Ltd.[14]

Among all firms listed a sample group was selected according to criteria designed to better control the interpretation of the results. The criteria were as follows:

1. The firm was classified as a class 1 common carrier in 1959.
2. The firm was primarily an inter-city carrier of general freight.
3. During the years 1953, 1959, and 1960, the reporting firm did not list any ownership entanglements with any other firm of any type.
4. A continuous series of yearly data was available for the firms for the years 1953 through 1960.

The first criterion specified type of business. The second narrowed the size grouping of interest. The third cut down possible bias in the reported figures resulting from interconnecting businesses. The last assured some degree of permanence in each firm's operations and reporting habits.

In all, seventy-two firms met the listed qualifications. The sample was therefore constituted by yearly data selected from this group of firms. Some idea of the size of the firms included is suggested by noting that the average and typical total assets amounted to $1,200,000 and $800,000 respectively for the year 1959. The average for all reporting class 1 carriers of a similar type in 1959 was about $2,400,000. Thus, the specification of no ownership complications forced the sample to represent a population of firms somewhat smaller than the over-all population of class 1 firms. Other suggestive 1959 summary statistics for the sample firms include average revenue of about $3,000,000, average haul of about 230 miles, and average weight per shipment of about .86 tons. As was the case with assets, the average revenue is smaller for the sample firms than for the group of all class 1 firms. The haul and weight per shipment are roughly comparable between the two groups.

For each firm in the sample, data were collected and analyzed for each of the years 1955 through 1960.[15] The use of more than one year's data was dictated by considerations mentioned earlier. That is, for one thing, computing the problem separately for several different years allowed an idea to be gained of the sensitivity of the results to the

18

particular period of estimation. In addition, some kind of averaged results could be derived which would summarize the relations observed over several periods. Finally, the use of more than one year's data was required in order to apply the method developed in the foregoing for correcting error bias. The use of no more than six years was a subjective decision arrived at through balancing the advantage of more data with the disadvantages of more cost and more doubt that the parameters would remain stable for the entire period.

The linear model hypothesis in the last section,

$$\log C = b_1 + b_2 \log O + b_3 \log W + b_4 \log H + U,$$

was fitted for each of the years 1955 through 1960 by using observations on the seventy-two selected firms. Justification for the single equation form of the cost model is conveniently provided by reference to the common carrier nature of the industry. In general, common carriers are required to carry all business that comes to them at the posted prices. Thus, it is primarily output that determines costs and not the other way around.[16]

The results of the standard least squares fitting process of the assumed cost model are displayed in Table 1. The parameter estimates appear directly under the appropriate letter at the top of the chart. The numbers in parentheses are the corresponding standard errors. R^2 signifies the coefficient of determination.

The main conclusion regarding the estimates in the different years is that they are much the same regardless of year. The estimated parameter for the log of shipments is always about .95, the estimated parameter for the log of weight is always about .70, and the estimated parameter for the log of haul is always about .31. This is evidence that the results are not peculiar to the year of estimation. (Note, however, that the six estimates should not be interpreted as reinforcing each other as if they were independent estimates. In fact the sample observations are much the same for all years since they were drawn from the same group of firms.) Thus there appears little reason why the estimates for the sample cannot be summarized in a single set of figures.

ECONOMIES OF SCALE IN TRUCKING

TABLE 1. Cross Section Cost Estimates By Year.
1955-1960 Cost Estimates.

$$\text{Log } C_t = b_1 + b_2 \text{ Log } O_t + b_3 \text{ Log } W_t + b_4 \text{ Log } H_t$$

Year t	R^2	$\hat{b}_1$	$\hat{b}_2$	$\hat{b}_3$	$\hat{b}_4$
1960	.946	.640	.932 (.027)	.670 (.035)	.323 (.030)
1959	.930	.605	.954 (.032)	.682 (.041)	.299 (.032)
1958	.942	.504	.945 (.029)	.670 (.037)	.359 (.031)
1957	.931	.680	.941 (.031)	.733 (.040)	.284 (.029)
1956	.942	.529	.955 (.030)	.726 (.035)	.320 (.027)
1955	.957	.511	.959 (.025)	.717 (.028)	.317 (.024)

To summarize the estimates, the following model was simultaneously fitted to all 432 observations.

$$\log C = b_1 + b_2 \log O + b_3 \log W + b_4 \log H + b_5 T + b_6 I_{56} + b_7 I_{57} + b_8 I_{58} + b_9 I_{59} + b_{10} I_{60} + \log U$$

The old variables are defined as before. Among the new variables, T stands for the per cent of tons billed at truck load rates. The addition of this variable was an attempt to improve the over-all fit through adding another dimension to the product description. The remaining new variables are defined as follows:

$$I_{56} = \begin{cases} 1 \text{ if the observation was for year 1956} \\ 0 \text{ if not} \end{cases}$$

$$I_{57} = \begin{cases} 1 \text{ if the observation was for year 1957} \\ 0 \text{ if not} \end{cases}$$

$$I_{58} = \begin{cases} 1 \text{ if the observation was for year 1958} \\ 0 \text{ if not} \end{cases}$$

$$I_{59} = \begin{cases} 1 \text{ if the observation was for year 1959} \\ 0 \text{ if not} \end{cases}$$

$$I_{60} = \begin{cases} 1 \text{ if the observation was for year 1960} \\ 0 \text{ if not} \end{cases}$$

The addition of the "I" variables essentially allowed the constant to be different for each year. For example, b_6, the estimated coefficient of I_{56}, summarizes the added effects on the log of cost peculiar to the year 1956. The estimated parameters for this model are shown in Table 2.

It was indicated in section 1.2 that some estimates which appear are subject to an estimation bias. Ignoring this for the minute allows an interpretation to be made of the results suggested by the estimates in the table. Later on the extent of the bias will be examined.

To take the estimated coefficient of the shipment variable first, it is clear that the magnitude of this uncorrected estimate suggests the presence of economies of scale. This is true since the estimate is several "standard errors" below 1. A coefficient of 1 would imply that— other things equal—a ten per cent increase in shipments would result in a ten per cent increase in costs. A coefficient of .95 implies that a ten per cent increase in shipment would result in only about a nine

TABLE 2. Combined Cross Section Cost Estimates.

$$\text{Log C} = b_1 + b_2 \text{ Log O} + b_3 \text{ Log W} + b_4 \text{ Log H} + b_5 \text{ T} + b_6 I_{56} + b_7 I_{57}$$
$$+ b_8 I_{58} + b_9 I_{59} + b_{10} I_{60}$$

R^2	$\hat{b_1}$	$\hat{b_2}$	$\hat{b_3}$	$\hat{b_4}$	$\hat{b_5}$	$\hat{b_6}$	$\hat{b_7}$	$\hat{b_8}$	$\hat{b_9}$	$\hat{b_{10}}$
.943	.574	.947	.742	.321	−.080	.017	.051	.055	.071	.094
		(.012)	(.024)	(.012)	(.035)	(.010)	(.010)	(.010)	(.010)	(.010)

and one-half per cent increase in total cost. The other things being equal of course refers to length of haul, weight per shipment, and per cent of tons received in truck load lots.

The estimated coefficient for length of haul suggests that—other things equal—a ten per cent increase in reported haul results in about a three per cent increase in total cost. On the other hand, the estimated coefficient for weight per shipment suggests that—other things equal—a ten per cent increase in reported weight per shipment tends to result in about a seven per cent increase in total cost. It is interesting to note that this asymmetry in the way average weight and haul affect costs suggests an alteration in the rule of thumb notion of output as corresponding to ton miles. That is, the effect of ton miles on cost is obviously different depending on whether these ton miles were generated by longer haul, greater weight, or simply more shipments. Supposing that a useful economic measure of output is one that is roughly proportional to cost, the study sample suggests a specific output index that should be much closer to economic output than is the notion of ton miles. The suggested index is $OW^{.7}H^{.3}.[17]$

In particular, the study suggests that a K percentage change in ton miles should be associated with about a (⅓) K percentage change in output if the increase comes through longer haul, about (⅔) K percentage change in output if the increase comes through heavier shipments, and of course a K per cent change in output if the increase comes solely through more shipments.

The estimated effect on cost of an increase in the percentage of truckload shipments—other things equal—appeared to be very small. This result was not unexpected, and indeed the expectation of this was the reason for omitting the per cent truck load variable from the first series of regressions. The reason for the small effect is suggested by remembering first of all that this coefficient is an estimate of the effects of more truck load shipments with scale and the other product dimensions held constant. In particular, the number of shipments and their average weight is being held constant. Now if it were true that all truck shipments tended to be of approximately equal density (weigh about the same per unit of volume), then a larger per cent of truck load shipments for fixed average weight would imply a more convenient distribution of shipment weights. Thus to this extent a greater per cent of truck load shipments would imply an easier carrying job. In other words, it would imply lower cost.

But in fact, it is not necessarily true that all truck shipments tend to be about the same weight per volume. It is then fairly straightforward that a greater per cent of truck load business—average shipment weight constant—may in part be associated with simply more or unwieldly bulk for fixed weight. With weight per shipment constant, more volume per shipment suggests lower average density. Thus to this extent the partial effect on costs should be so much the higher.

A priori it is not at all clear that the two opposing effects should nearly balance out. In the present study, however, the net effect was virtually zero. An absolute increase of ten percentage points in the truck load business was estimated to result on average in about .008 decline in the log of cost. This would be less than one tenth of a percentage point decline in cost.

The remainder of the parameter estimates can be interpreted as reflecting the influence of all omitted factors upon cost during the period of study. For example, $\hat{b}_1 = .574$ summarizes the net effects on the log of cost in 1955 of all other influences besides average weight, length of haul, number of shipments, and per cent of business received in truck load lots. The effect of all omitted factors upon the log of 1956 costs is clearly $\hat{b}_1 + \hat{b}_6 = .574 + .017 = .591$. The net influence of the omitted factors in the other years is developed in a similar manner. Thus the net effects on the log of 1957 costs are .625, on the log of 1958 costs are .629, on the log of 1959 costs are .645 and on the log of 1960 costs are .668.

It is clear from these figures that the net effect of omitted factors tended to increase costs during each of the succeeding years included in the study. That is, after allowing for year-to-year changes in costs due to differences in haul, weight of shipment, per cent of truck load business, and number of shipments, it turns out that there was still an upward drift of costs due to other causes.

The extent of this cost drift can be illustrated by converting the estimated yearly impact on the log of costs to an estimated yearly impact on costs themselves. To compare 1956 costs with 1955 costs for example, an inspection of the estimated cost equation shows the log 1956 costs greater by .017 than the log of 1955 costs. This is equivalent to the log $\dfrac{1956 \text{ costs}}{1955 \text{ costs}} = .017$ or in other words that the ratio

of 1956 costs to 1955 costs was $10^{.017}$ or 1.04. Thus in terms of 1955 costs, 1956 costs were up by four per cent. Similarly, as compared with 1955 costs

> 1957 costs were up by 12 per cent,
> 1958 costs were up by 14 per cent,
> 1959 costs were up by 18 per cent, and
> 1960 costs were up by 24 per cent.

During the period examined there was therefore an over-all upward drift in costs of about 24 per cent. If the product description is reasonably complete, this would suggest a roughly corresponding drift in input prices. It might also reflect the provision of some additional services not allowed for by the product index.

1.6 EFFECTS OF BIAS

In the theoretical section the effects of the "short run" bias were declared to primarily affect the constant term of regression relationships. Thus, the coefficients most under suspicion from this source of bias are $\hat{b}_1$ and $\hat{b}_6$ through $\hat{b}_{10}$. However, a check can be made for evidence of skew in the distribution of the residuals from the computed regressions. If the true distribution is greatly asymmetrical, this might well be evidenced by a skewed distribution of the residuals. A count of observed negative residuals versus a count of positive residuals might therefore suggest the seriousness of this type of bias for particular cases. In order to perform some such check in this study the residuals for each of the original six regressions listed earlier were computed and examined. The results appear in Table 3. An inspection of the table shows the number of negative residuals is virtually the same as the number of positive residuals. Thus this check provides no evidence of substantial bias due to the "short run" bias.

At any rate, the bias due to the "short run" effects ordinarily need not affect the other parameters. In particular it should not affect the estimate of the output coefficient—the estimate indicating the presence or absence of economies of scale. Indeed this was part of the

TABLE 3. Comparison of Residuals For The
1955-1960 Cost Estimates.

Year	Number of Negative Residuals	Number of Positive Residuals
1960	36	36
1959	33	39
1958	31	41
1957	36	36
1956	35	37
1955	35	37

reason for preferring the logarithmic formulation. The same cannot be said, however, of the bias due to error in the output variable. To what extent is there apt to be bias from this source?

It is conceivable that the output for some industries could be so close to homogeneous and so accurately reported that there would be no measurement error in the output variable. For most cost studies, however, it is probable that any variable identified as representing economic output will at best be an approximation to economic output. This is certainly true for the industry associated with general trucking services. No matter how many particular dimensions of the product are allowed for there are apt to be others which are not allowed for. Thus any variable identified as trucking "output"—even with certain key product dimensions controlled—is subject to measurement error. Accordingly, in the model for trucking services the variable, "number of shipments," must be considered subject to measurement error when interpreted as the "output" variable.

In Section 1.2 the problem of error bias was discussed and dealt with by reference to the simplest version of the log-linear cost function, that is, the model in which only two variables are involved. It is therefore clear that the results of the estimation section cannot be directly applied to the model for trucking services. This is true since the model employed for estimating cost of trucking services involves many more variables than simply a single output and cost variable. The method used for reducing the problem to a two variable problem can be understood through the considerations outlined in the following paragraphs. It is to be emphasized, however, that the method is directed only toward removing the bias in the coefficient of the output variable.

Define a hypothetical true *adjusted* cost figure for each firm that incorporates the effects of all variables but that of shipments. This new cost, denoted by c_{tj} instead of C_{tj}, refers to a firm's reported cost plus or minus certain adjustments depending upon what firm and time period are involved. The adjustments make specific allowance for differences in length of haul, average weight, per cent of truck load business, and time periods. The allowances are made so as to permit the comparison of the cost and output data for different firms and different time periods.

Next, estimate $\log c_{tj}$ by $\log \hat{C}_{tj}$ where $\log \hat{C}_{tj}$ is calculated through the use of the estimated relationship already developed. In particular, use Table 2 to define the estimated *adjusted* log cost of firm j at time t as

(22) $\log \hat{C}_{tj} = \log C_{tj} - .574 - .742 \log W_{tj} - .321 \log H_{tj} + .080 T_{tj} - b_t$

where C_{tj} was the reported total cost; W_{tj}, H_{tj}, and T_{tj} were as in Table 2 and

$$
\begin{aligned}
b_t &= .000 \text{ for the estimate corresponding to the year 1955} \\
&= .017 \text{ for } t = 6 \quad \text{(corresponding to the year 1956)} \\
&= .051 \text{ for } t = 7 \quad \text{(corresponding to the year 1957)} \\
&= .055 \text{ for } t = 8 \quad \text{(corresponding to the year 1958)} \\
&= .071 \text{ for } t = 9 \quad \text{(corresponding to the year 1959)} \\
&= .094 \text{ for } t = 10 \quad \text{(corresponding to the year 1960).}
\end{aligned}
$$

Now considering the two variable regression

(23) $\qquad\qquad \log \hat{C}_{tj} = b \log O_{tj} + v_{tj},$

several things may be noted. First, the variable $\log \hat{C}_{tj}$ may be associated with the true *adjusted* cost notion $\log c_{tj}$ but not as an errorless approximation. Second, the variable $\log O_{tj}$ may similarly be associated with a true economic output but not as an errorless approximation. Third, the least squares estimation of b in the foregoing two variable regression using all 432 observations would be identically equal to the coefficient of the log of shipments already estimated in the expanded relationship. That is, the estimate of b would be equal to the estimate of b_2 set out in table 2. Thus these remarks allow the trucking services model and estimates to be interpretable within the error analysis framework discussed in the estimation section.

This implies, in particular, that the estimate of b_2 in Table 2—the coefficient of the log of shipments—is subject to a negative bias. It suggests that this estimate tends to overstate the case for economies of scale.

In Section 1.2 a method was suggested for correcting the bias through estimating a "through time" relationship corresponding to the estimated cross section relationship. The cross section's first difference relationship that would correspond to equation (23) is

(24) $\log \hat{C}_{tj} - \log \hat{C}_{pj} = d(\log O_{tj} - \log O_{pj}) + k + (v_{tj} - v_{pj})$.

Suppose that (t-p) is chosen so as to allow d to be considered an estimate of the long run relationship. Then the error model developed earlier can be used to compute the adjustment that should be made to allow for measurement error in the output variable. Thus to develop the adjustment for this error the following procedure was carried out.

1. A year t and a previous p were selected.
2. Log $\hat{C}_{tj}$ and log $\hat{C}_{pj}$ were computed exactly as defined by equation (22) for each of the seventy-two firms.
3. (Log $\hat{C}_{tj}$ − log $\hat{C}_{pj}$) and (log O_{tj} − log O_{pj}) were computed for each of the seventy-two firms.
4. The regression implied by (24) was accomplished with the observations computed in 3. The resulting estimate of d was interpreted as a long run output coefficient comparable to b.
5. The formulas developed in the estimation section were then applied so as to estimate the variance of the measurement error and the implied appropriate correction to the output coefficient.

6. The estimates of d and b were adjusted upward accordingly.

In accomplishing this error-correcting procedure, some arbitrariness centered about the selection of a proper period to allow for "long run" adjustment. Fortunately, unlike most industries, firms in the trucking industry should be able to make full long run adjustments in comparatively few years. For upward adjustments in output it is relatively easy to purchase or lease additional trucks on short notice. For adjustments downward there is the factor that normal operations require the replacement of a substantial part of the assets each year. Thus downward adjustments can be accomplished rather easily by simply not replacing at the normal rate. When such factors as these are considered it seems reasonable to suppose that a three or four year period is probably long enough to correspond to a long run adjustment in the trucking industry. For the actual investigation three different time gaps were tried. Table 4 shows that the parameter estimates were computed on the basis of cross section estimates using three, four, and five year time differences.[18] The table also shows the implied error variance that is suggested by each time gap. Finally, of course, it shows the corresponding corrected estimate of the long run output coefficient. It is interesting to note that the correction applied by the error model in no case resulted in a change of the implication that economies of scale were present.

While it is impossible to directly assess the relevance of the assumptions of the error model used, it is reassuring to note that a main implication of the error model is borne out directly by the data. That is, the basic error model states that the downward bias should be more serious the more the variance of the "independent" variable is constituted solely by error variance. The formulas in the estimation section implied that the bias should be much more serious in cross section models involving time differences.[19] Taking for granted that the true output parameter is somewhere near unity, it is clear from Table 4 that the bias was indeed much more serious in the first difference regressions. All the cross section regressions of differences had substantially greater bias than any of the six regular cross section regressions listed earlier. This is evidenced by the uncorrected estimated output coefficients of .66, .75, and .88 for the time gaps of three, four, and five years respectively. After correction for error the .66

28

TABLE 4. Auxiliary First Difference Cost Estimates and Adjusted Output Coefficients.

$$\text{Log } \hat{C}_t - \text{Log } \hat{C}_p = k + d[\text{Log } O_t - \text{Log } O_p]$$

Year		R^2	$\hat{k}$	$\hat{d}$	$\hat{\sigma}^2[\text{Log}(O_t/O_p)]$	$\hat{\sigma}^2(\text{Log } O_t)$	$\hat{b}_2$	$\hat{\sigma}^2(f_t)$
t	p							
60	57	.72	.005	.660 (.049)	.02509	.11090	.947	.00414
60	56	.91	.002	.750 (.027)	.03419	.11090	.947	.00404
60	55	.90	.003	.882 (.034)	.02418	.11090	.947	.00092

Year		$\dfrac{\hat{\sigma}^2(f_t)}{\hat{\sigma}^2(\text{Log } O_t) - \hat{\sigma}^2(f_t)}$	$\dfrac{2\hat{\sigma}^2(f_t)}{\hat{\sigma}^2[\text{Log}(O_t/O_p)] - 2\hat{\sigma}^2(f_t)}$	$\text{Adj } \hat{b}_2 = \text{Adj } \hat{d}$
t	p			
60	57	.039	.490	.983
60	56	.038	.309	.982
60	55	.008	.082	.955

estimate became .98, the .75 estimate became .98, and the .88 estimate became .955. The correction for the cross section ·947 estimate was, of course, also raised accordingly.

The remarkable differences implied in the error variances between regular cross section and first difference observations was one of the most interesting results of the error model. The ratio of error variances to true output variance was estimated from .008 to .039 for the regular cross section data. The same ratio for the cross section first difference formulation was estimated from .082 to .490! This has interesting methodological implications for other first difference type

29

of regressions. In particular, measurement error bias is greatly compounded in regressions of first differences.

After the adjustments to the output coefficient, the results still imply certain economies of scale. To show the order of magnitude of these estimates a graphical comparison is exhibited in Figure 1 displaying the estimated average cost of a given type of shipment at different levels of output. The type of shipment is one of about ⅔ of a ton going a distance of approximately 190 miles. (These were the geometric means of the sample observations.) The data reflect costs generally appropriate for the year 1960,[20] and the cost parameter was taken to be .97 for illustrative purposes. To give a more conventional

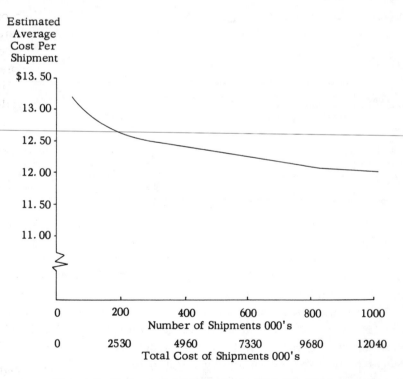

Figure 1. Estimated 1960 Average Cost Per Shipment of ⅔ Ton Going a Distance of 190 Miles—based on b_2 = .97.

idea of the size of the firms involved, total cost of shipments is plotted along with number of shipments. As can be seen, the implied average costs drop from about $13.00 to $12.00 over the indicated range of outputs. This gives an idea of the order of magnitude of economies of scale if the true parameter is somewhere in the neighborhood of .97.

1.7 ESTIMATES REGARDING INDIVIDUAL COST COMPONENTS

In the standard reporting forms the items of trucking cost are broken into several components. While classification methods could be expected to vary somewhat for individual firms, the accounts are fairly well standardized through the use of elaborate reporting forms and directions. Thus it is also of interest to explore the relation of these individual cost components to output changes. The results of these estimates suggest hypotheses as to the types of costs that are and are not subject to economies of scale. Having already developed an estimate of the variance of the error term in the output variable, it is a straightforward task to compute and correct the output coefficient that is appropriate to each major component of cost. The adjusted results are tabulated in Table 5.

Essentially the same independent variables were used as were used for the total cost estimates. The individual cost components should depend for the most part on the same factors as total costs—length of haul, weight per shipment, per cent of tons by truck load shipments, and scale of output. However, the firms that accomplished a relatively larger per cent of their business in rented equipment might well have their individual cost components varying differently from those firms who used more owned equipment. For example, depreciation expense should be relatively greater for firms using their own trucks than for firms renting them. In order to help control such differences arising from the rent or buy option, an additional variable was introduced. This variable was the per cent of vehicle miles accomplished by owned equipment. This variable is designated M in Table 5.

The estimated coefficients that appear in the chart are interpreted substantially as before. To take the coefficients of the output variable first, it is seen that the estimated coefficients fall roughly into three

TABLE 5. Combined Cross Section
Cost-Component Estimates.

$$\text{Log Cost Component} = c_1 + c_2 \text{ Log } O + c_3 \text{ Log } W + c_4 \text{ Log } H + c_5 T + c_6 I_{56} + c_7 I_{57} + c_8 I_{58} + c_9 I_{59} + c_{10} I_{60} + c_{11} M$$

	R^2	$\hat{c}_1$	adj $\hat{c}_2$	$\hat{c}_3$	$\hat{c}_4$	$\hat{c}_5$	$\hat{c}_6$	$\hat{c}_7$	$\hat{c}_8$	$\hat{c}_9$	$\hat{c}_{10}$	$\hat{c}_{11}$
Maintenance Costs	.69	-1.278	1.124 (.038)	.804 (.079)	.253 (.039)	.417 (.115)	.004 (.034)	.024 (.034)	.014 (.034)	.065 (.034)	.065 (.034)	.486 (.035)
Transportation Costs	.91	.459	.907 (.015)	.798 (.031)	.319 (.015)	-.119 (.045)	.013 (.013)	.053 (.013)	.059 (.013)	.075 (.013)	.093 (.013)	-.115 (.013)
Terminal Costs	.88	-.735	1.162 (.022)	.612 (.047)	.303 (.023)	-.132 (.068)	.014 (.019)	.064 (.019)	.084 (.019)	.095 (.020)	.130 (.020)	.074 (.021)
Traffic Costs	.66	-.819	.948 (.035)	.777 (.072)	.282 (.036)	.034 (.105)	.025 (.031)	.096 (.031)	.123 (.031)	.095 (.031)	.120 (.031)	-.018 (.032)
Insurance Costs	.81	-.698	.860 (.022)	.638 (.045)	.398 (.022)	-.102 (.065)	-.006 (.019)	.011 (.019)	.014 (.019)	.037 (.019)	.068 (.019)	-.028 (.020)
Administration Costs	.68	.018	.727 (.025)	.419 (.052)	.246 (.025)	.043 (.075)	.025 (.022)	-.028 (.022)	-.021 (.022)	-.020 (.022)	-.024 (.022)	.056 (.023)
Depreciation Costs	.73	-1.933	1.050 (.034)	.825 (.071)	.605 (.034)	-.023 (.101)	.061 (.029)	.107 (.029)	.113 (.029)	.071 (.030)	.101 (.029)	.321 (.031)
Tax Costs	.84	-1.067	1.009 (.023)	.720 (.047)	.320 (.023)	.023 (.068)	.040 (.019)	.085 (.019)	.088 (.020)	.106 (.020)	.153 (.020)	.256 (.021)

groups. There are those that are well above 1, those that are just about 1, and those that are below 1. These three groups indicate cost rising more than proportional to output, cost rising about in proportion to output, and cost rising less than proportional to output respectively.

Maintenance and terminal costs fall into the first group. Both of these types of cost appeared to increase more than in proportion to output. The fact that terminal costs rise more than in proportion to output probably is in part a reflection of the tendency of larger firms to do more consolidating of shipments. The fact that maintenance costs seem to rise more than in proportion to output is somewhat surprising but very much in evidence in the study.

Depreciation and taxes seem to rise very nearly in proportion to increases in output. The adjusted coefficients were 1.05 and 1.00 respectively. It is reasonable that tax rates should not depend on size, and the sample evidence suggests that about the same amount of trucks are used up per unit of output at all output levels.

The estimated coefficients relating output to transportation expense and output to traffic expense are below 1, and they are roughly the same order of magnitude as those found to relate output to total costs. Inasmuch as transportation costs make up 50 per cent of total costs and have a coefficient well below 1, it is savings from this source that appear to dominate the relation between output and total costs. It is interesting to note that this is where one would expect savings from scheduling and routing advantages to accumulate.

Finally, the coefficients of insurance and administrative costs appear well below 1. The low insurance coefficient of .86 was not unexpected due to economies of scale in the purchase of insurance and possibly due to some tendency on the part of larger firms to self-insure. The coefficient of administration costs is lowest of all at .73! The fact that costs of coordination and administration are often cited as ones to watch for possible diseconomies of scale makes this result interesting indeed. That is, far from being a source of diseconomies, administrative costs prove to be a source of economies of scale. It may be that the coordination difficulties show up in other accounts such as maintenance expense. Or it may be that the coordination difficulties of size have largely dissipated as a result of modern improvements in data processing and communication.

Most of the other coefficients in the chart require no discussion inasmuch as they are of secondary interest for the study. In comparing the effects of reported haul and reported weight it can be noted that with the exception of administrative and depreciation costs, given percentage changes in weight per shipment have about two or three times the effect of the same percentage changes in haul.

A final note of interest is the drift in the component of cost identified with taxes. It is readily apparent that there has been more drift in this component of cost than any other. As compared with 1955 experience, the log of tax cost had drifted a $+ .15$ by 1960. This would imply that the ratio of tax costs after adjusting for output changes was equal to $10^{.15}$. Roughly speaking, this would imply that the tax rates on economic output were up on the order of 40 per cent in the five year period. Since taxes are roughly ten per cent of total costs this is a substantial increase in over-all costs.

1.8 RELATION OF OPERATING RATIOS TO OUTPUT

The estimated relations between costs and output suggest that operating ratios should also tend to be lower at larger outputs. If the average cost of a given type of shipment declines with output while average revenue remains much the same, then obviously the ratio of average cost to average revenue should also decline. So operating ratios should decline.

In introducing revenue into the analysis, however, it is important to note that average revenue per a certain type of shipment is not necessarily the same for all firms. The national tariff structure is complicated and capricious. Thus while operating ratios depend partly on relative cost advantage, they depend partly on relative tariff advantage, and the two effects need not go together. This suggests that the relation between operating ratios and output will be weak at best.

The relation between operating ratios and output was estimated in a manner exactly analogous to the cost model. The log of the operating ratio was regressed upon the log of shipments, weight, haul, and the per cent of truck load shipments. The results appear in Table 6.

The small value of R^2 attests to the weakness of the relation. In effect, output doesn't explain much of the observable variance in operating ratios. The individual relations are also more tenuous than was the case with the cost analysis but still sizeable in terms of their standard errors.

TABLE 6. Combined Cross Section
Operating Ratio Estimates.

$$\text{Log } C - \text{Log } R = r_1 + r_2 \text{ Log } O + r_3 \text{ Log } W + r_4 \text{ Log } H + r_5 T + r_6 I_{56}$$
$$+ r_7 I_{57} + r_8 I_{58} + r_9 I_{59} + r_{10} I_{60}$$

R^2	$\hat{r}_1$	$\hat{r}_2$	$\hat{r}_3$	$\hat{r}_4$	$\hat{r}_5$	$\hat{r}_6$	$\hat{r}_7$	$\hat{r}_8$	$\hat{r}_9$	$\hat{r}_{10}$
.17	.042	-.011	-.015	-.022	.012	.005	.007	.009	.008	.016
		(.003)	(.006)	(.003)	(.009)	(.003)	(.003)	(.003)	(.003)	(.003)

Taking the estimates at face value, several hypotheses are suggested by these results. The first is that the estimated effect of output upon profitability is markedly weaker than its effect upon costs alone. This is true since the estimate here of -.011 implies that a 100 per cent change in output results in only about a one per cent decline in operating ratio. The same change in output was estimated to result in about a three to five per cent decline in costs. One possible explanation for this is that the product of large firms is priced closer to cost than is the product of small firms. An alternate explanation is that a part of the estimated lower costs at high outputs is attributable to some feature of product which was not explicitly allowed for. That is, some feature of product that is associated with both lower cost and lower revenue may also be associated with large firms. The latter argument would imply that the estimates in the cost section over-estimated economies of scale.

The parameter estimate -.011 is of course subject to an error bias just as the output coefficient was in the cost analysis. Since the output error variance is already estimated, the .011 estimate can be corrected for this bias. The correction in this case case does not much matter, however, since the corrected estimate is -.0112. Thus, corrected or uncorrected, the estimate is on the order of .01. To see the type of change that is implied by this number, a comparison can be constructed analogous to the cost and output comparison of Figure 1. The same assumptions as to year and product are made as before. Figure 2 illustrates the relation. As before, approximate total cost figures accompany the shipment figures for ease in interpreting size of concern. The general level of the operating ratios is the result of the choice of the weight and haul as ⅔ ton and 190 miles respectively. The gradual decline from about 1.00 to .975 is the implied effect of changes in output. If the true parameter is about .01, this is the order of magnitude of effects that should be expected.

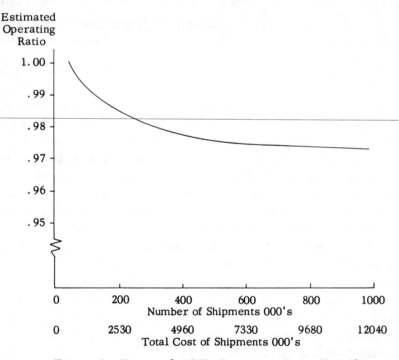

Figure 2. Estimated 1960 Operating Ratio For Shipments of ⅔ Ton Going a Distance of 190 Miles—based on r_2 = .01.

36

The remainder of the estimates in Table 6 are interesting for the implications regarding the relative profitability of carrying different types of shipments. The coefficient of the weight variable implies that a 100 per cent increase in weight per shipment is associated with about a minus 1.5 per cent change in operating ratio. The effect of 100 per cent increase in haul is estimated to result in about a minus 2.2 per cent change in the same ratio. These variables suggest that— at least for the sample period—the extra cost of carrying heavier and long haul shipments was more than compensated by the extra revenue that these shipments generated. Stated otherwise, the existing tariff structure put a premium on carrying these types of shipments. Given average weight and length of haul, however, the results suggested that the cost advantages of more truck load shipments were largely offset by lower rates charged for such shipments. The comments advanced earlier concerning interpretation of the truck load variable make this last result not surprising.

A final note concerns the time drift of operating ratios after allowing for scale effects and changes in type of product. With the sole exception of the year 1959 (an unusually good year) the operating ratios of the sample firms edged up every year involved in the study.

1.9 PERFORMANCE OF INDIVIDUAL FIRMS

All the results thus far have involved relationships interpretable as pertaining to some average or representative trucking firm. In general these results were secured through comparing the costs and outputs of different firms with each other. It is therefore natural to ask if there is any evidence regarding the relationships for individual firms that might support or refute the hypothesis of economies of scale.

Were the time series long enough, it would be possible to compute parameter estimates for individual firms and compare these with the general cross section estimates. Because they are not long enough, it is unlikely that such estimates could be derived with any precision. Since, however, direction as well as magnitude is of interest, it is sensible to make some decision for each firm as to whether or not its particular performance would suggest the presence of economies of scale.

This was accomplished through the following considerations. During the study period of 1955 through 1960, each firm generally made some over-all expansion or contraction in its business. Similarly, the firm would have reported an over-all change in operating ratios for the period. Roughly speaking, if the expanding firms would be associated with declining operating ratios and the contracting firms would be associated with increasing operating ratios, the results would suggest economies of scale. Table 7 exhibits a comparison for the seventy-two firms in the sample for the 1955 to 1960 period. Before the comparison, the parameter estimates of the cross section regression were used to adjust the change in operating ratios for changes in product dimension and average temporal drift.

It is evident from the table that during the period twenty-nine firms contracted output while 43 expanded output. Of the twenty-nine firms reporting declines in output, eighteen or sixty-two per cent reported an increase in operating ratios for the period. Of the forty-three expanding firms, thirty or seventy per cent, reported a decrease in operating ratios. Thus, in either bracket about two-thirds of the

TABLE 7. Expansion and Contraction Compared
To Change In Operating Ratios.

	36 Smallest Firms in Sample		36 Largest Firms in Sample	
	Operating Ratio Improved (Declined)	Operating Ratio Increased	Operating Ratio Improved (Declined)	Operating Ratio Increased
Expanding Firms	14	5	16	8
Contracting Firms	8	9	3	9

observations suggested economies of scale. Of some additional interest is the fact that the experience of the thirty-six biggest firms in the sample was comparable to that of the thirty-six smallest. Of the smallest firms, twenty-three, or sixty-five per cent, suggested the presence of economies of scale. Of the thirty-six largest firms, twenty-five, or seventy per cent, suggested the presence of economies of scale.

1.10 CONCLUSIONS

A conclusion about theoretical cost models concerned the importance of recognizing the existence of short run phenomena in all observed cost figures. If not allowed for, the short run effects may bias the estimations and create interpretation difficulties. Most of the difficulties can be recognized by visualizing the random term in the typical cost model as containing both a short run component and an error component.

The main methodological innovation was the method developed for correcting for measurement errors in the independent variable of a regression relationship. The method allowed consistent estimates to be derived for the variance of those measurement errors and for the coefficient relating the true independent and dependent variables. The method proved remarkably simple to apply and interpret.

In applying the combined cost and error model to trucking costs, a point of interest concerned how effectively the error model resolved the observed differences between ordinary cross section estimates and cross section estimates derived through first differences. The ordinary uncorrected cross section estimates were about .95, while the uncorrected first difference estimates of the same parameter were only .66, .75, and .88. But when allowance was made for measurement errors as indicated by the error model, these sizeable differences between the uncorrected estimates turned out to be largely explained by measurement errors in the output variable. That is, after correction for measurement errors, all the first difference estimates also implied parameters of about .95! These results suggest that this measurement error model may be useful in other studies. The results also suggest some of the inherent measurement error difficulties in general first difference regressions.

In applying the cost model to the empirical data, the number of shipments, average weight, and average haul turned out to offer a reasonably complete explanation of the costs of the firms in the sample. Ignoring for the moment the economies of scale, the estimated relationship was found to indicate total cost to be roughly proportional to

$$(\text{shipments}) \left(\frac{\text{tons}}{\text{shipments}}\right)^{.7} \left(\frac{\text{ton miles}}{\text{tons}}\right)^{.3}$$

with the proportionality factor depending on the year. This would imply that a ten per cent increase in average shipment weight would tend to be associated with a seven per cent change in average shipment cost; and that a ten per cent change in average haul would tend to be associated with a three per cent change in average shipment cost. The dependence of total revenue upon output was found to follow much the same pattern, but the difference between the cost and revenue function was such as to suggest that the heavier and longer haul shipments would be the more profitable ones.

As suggested earlier, the interpretation of the empirical results concerning economies of scale should be tempered by the fact that a different approach might have resulted in different conclusions. This is unavoidable in an industry where the conclusions turn on such small differences. With that qualification, the results clearly suggested economies of scale. All phases of the investigation were much more consistent with that hypothesis than the other way around. Several considerations suggested the economies were not as large as they appeared to be in the first set of uncorrected estimates. The results with the operating ratios were particularly telling in this respect. But while different sections suggested a different level of economies as being appropriate, all sections provided evidence of at least some economies. The smallest estimate suggested that, other things equal, operating ratios should decline about .01 for a doubling of output.

As to whether the economies suggested are large or small, it all depends upon what is being argued. Certainly the economies suggested are not overpowering in the sense that such differences as there are cannot be overcome by a favorably situated small firm. The main determinant of profitability in the trucking business is the nature of the collection of shipments for which a firm is lucky or unlucky enough to be in line. A fortuitous enough set of shipments would probably allow even a single truck operator to compete.

On the other hand, the study does suggest that any *given* physical set of shipments is apt to be carried more cheaply by a combined firm than by a number of firms. The order of magnitude of the estimates implies that this cost difference is not likely to be great percentage wise, but the prevailing narrow margins greatly magnify the resultant effect on profits. Thus, whether a firm services a convenient and highly profitable set of shipments or an inconvenient profitless set, it is apt to find that its business is worth more when combined with that of another firm. At least for the size of the firms represented by the sample, there appear to be some natural forces working for combinations and mergers.

NOTES

1. Studies consistent with this conclusion include:

    Robert A. Nelson, *Motor Freight Transport in New England, A Report to the New England Governor's Council.* (Boston, 1956);

    Merill J. Roberts, "Some Aspects of Motor Carrier Costs: Firm Size, Efficiency, and Financial Health," *Land Economics,* vol. 32, no. 3, (August 1956), pp. 228-238;

    Walter Adams and James Hendry, *Trucking Mergers, Concentration and Small Business: An Analysis of Interstate Commerce Commission Policy, 1950-1956.* (Washington, Committee Print, Select Committee on Small Business of the United States Senate, 1956).

    John R. Meyer, Morton J. Peck, John Stenason, Charles Zwick, *The Economics of Competition in the Transportation Industries,* (Cambridge: Harvard University Press, 1959), pp. 64-110.

2. A representative statement is that of Meyer, et al., *ibid.*, p. 95, "It is, then, the length of haul and not size per se that explains most cost differences between firms."

3. The ratio of costs to revenue is ordinarily above .95. Thus while a one per cent change in costs is a small percentage reduction in costs, it permits a twenty per cent increase in profit margins!

4. J. Johnston, *Statistical Cost Analysis*, (New York: McGraw-Hill Book Company, Inc., 1960).

5. A proof of these more or less familiar results can be found in J. Johnston, *Econometric Methods*, (New York: McGraw-Hill Book Company, Inc., 1963), p. 148-150.

6. The classical bounding method is accomplished through interchanging the independent and dependent variables in separate regressions. A description is furnished by Johnston. (*ibid.*, pp. 150-156).

7. Various grouping methods are developed in A. Wald, "The Fitting of Straight Lines If Both Variables Are Subject to Error," (*Ann. Math. Statist.*, vol. 11, 1940), pp. 284-300.

   M. S. Bartlett, "The Fitting of Straight Lines if Both Variables Are Subject to Error," *Biometrics*, vol. 5, 1949, pp. 207-242.

   J. W. Hooper and H. Theil, "The Extensions of Wald's Method of Fitting Straight Lines to Multiple Regression," *Rev. Inter. Statist. Inst.*, 1958.

   J. W. Tukey, "Components in Regression," *Biometrics*, 7 (1951), pp. 33-70.

   Albert Madansky, "The Fitting of Straight Lines When Both Variables Are Subject to Error," *Journal of the American Statistical Association*, 54 (1959), 173-205.

8. Johnston, *Econometric Methods*, p. 165.

9. Gerhard Tintner, *Econometrics*, (New York: John Wiley & Sons, Inc., 1952), p. 135.

10. $$\text{adj } \hat{b} - \text{adj } \hat{d} = \hat{b}\left[1 + \frac{\hat{\sigma}^2(f_t)}{\hat{\sigma}^2(O_t) - \hat{\sigma}^2(f_t)}\right] - \hat{d}\left[1 + \frac{2\hat{\sigma}^2(f_t)}{\hat{\sigma}^2(O_t - O_p) - 2\hat{\sigma}^2(f_t)}\right]$$

$$= \frac{\hat{b}(\hat{\sigma}^2(O_t))[\hat{\sigma}^2(O_t - O_p) - 2\hat{\sigma}^2(f_t)] - \hat{d}(\hat{\sigma}^2(O_t - O_p))[\hat{\sigma}^2(O_t) - \hat{\sigma}^2(f_t)]}{[\hat{\sigma}^2(O_t) - \hat{\sigma}^2(f_t)][\hat{\sigma}^2(O_t - O_p) - 2\hat{\sigma}^2(f_t)]}$$

The numerator of the above fraction is

$$\hat{\sigma}^2 (f_t) [-2\hat{b}\hat{\sigma}^2 (O_t) + \hat{d}\hat{\sigma}^2 (O_t\text{-}O_p)] + [(\hat{\sigma}^2 (O_t)) (\hat{\sigma}^2 (O_t\text{-}O_p))] (\hat{b} - \hat{d});$$

and substituting for $\hat{\sigma}^2 (f_t)$ from its definition in expression (17) shows that this numerator is 0.

Thus adj $\hat{b}$ = adj $\hat{d}$.

11. Note the average haul is $\Sigma\, T_i M_i / \Sigma\, T_i$, where T_i and M_i are respectively the weight and haul of the ith shipment. Thus average haul is trip lengths weighted by the per cent of total tonnage going each length.

12. The variable U is the random factor. The other variables refer to the ICC definitions of the respective quantities. In particular

    C = total operating cost,

    O = total number of shipments,

    W = weight per shipment, and

    H = average haul.

13. It is a familiar fact from aggregation theory that the appropriateness of a micro model with micro data does not necessarily imply the appropriateness of the aggregated data. But the suggestion is clear.

14. *Trinc's Blue Book of the Trucking Industry*, published annually. (Washington, D.C.: Trinc Associates, Ltd.).

15. The list of the firms used appears in the Appendix. For each firm, the yearly total shipments, the total tons, the total ton-miles, the total cost by components, the total revenue, and the per cent of tons billed at truck load rates were compiled directly from Trinc's for each of the six years. Interpolated figures were substituted for a few obvious misprints.

16. For a rationale supporting the usefulness of single equation cost models in more general situations see J. Johnston, *Statistical Cost Analysis*, pp. 26-43.

17. Shipments is taken with geometrical weight equal to 1 because the presence or absence of economies of scale is a production— not a product phenomenon.

18. The relation between the symbols in Table 4 and the symbols in estimation formulas (17), (18), and (19) is as follows:

$\hat{b}_2$ of the chart corresponds to $\hat{b}$ of the formulas

$\hat{d}$ of the chart corresponds to $\hat{d}$ of the formulas

$\hat{\sigma}^2 (f_t)$ of the chart corresponds to $\hat{\sigma}^2 (f_t)$ of the formulas

$\hat{\sigma}^2 (\text{Log } O_t)$ of the chart corresponds to $\hat{\sigma}^2 (O_t)$ of the formulas

$\hat{\sigma}^2 \left(\text{Log } \dfrac{O_t}{O_p}\right)$ of the chart corresponds to $\hat{\sigma}^2 (O_t - O_p)$ of the formulas

The estimates $\hat{b}_2$ and $\hat{\sigma}^2 (\text{Log } O_t)$ in Table 4 were taken from the combined regression described by Table 2.

19. The bias is greater the greater the ratio of the variance of the error component to the variance of the true component. Examining the statements of bias in (12) and (13), it can be seen that the bias in the first difference estimates depends on $\dfrac{\sigma^2 (f_t - f_p)}{\sigma^2 (O_t - O_p)}$

while the bias in the regular estimates depends on $\dfrac{\sigma^2 (f_t)}{\sigma^2 (O_t)}$

Comparing these two expressions, it is to be noted that $\sigma^2 (f_t - f_p)$ will be greater than $\sigma^2 (f_t)$ [actually assumed to be twice $\sigma^2 (f_t)$] because of the relative independence of the two terms. On the other hand, o_t and o_p are far from independent because of the fact that the output of a given firm in year t is intimately related to its output in year p! Thus, the expression $\sigma^2 (o_t - o_p)$ should be much smaller in relation to $\sigma^2 (o_t)$ than $\sigma^2 (f_t - f_p)$ is to $\sigma^2 (f_t)$. In other words

$$\frac{\sigma^2 (f_t - f_p)}{\sigma^2 (o_t - o_p)} > \frac{\sigma^2 (f_t)}{\sigma^2 (o_t)} \; ; \quad \text{and}$$

the bias in the first difference estimation should be greater. Increasing (t-p) should reduce the effect through weakening the covariance between o_t and o_p.

20. Because the estimated constant in the estimated equations is different for different years, the absolute level of costs should be different for different years. It is also important to realize that the statistical qualities of the relationship are weaker on the ends of the curve.

APPENDIX

Common Carrier Trucking Firms in the Sample

A. Towle Company, Charlestown, Mass.
AAA Trucking Corporation, Trenton, N.J.
Aakins Transfer Company, Inc., Nashville, Tenn.
Allegheny Freight Lines, Inc., Winchester, Va.
Anderson Motor Service, Inc., St. Louis, Mo.
Baltimore-New York Express, Inc., Baltimore, Md.
Be-Mac Transport Company, Inc., St. Louis, Mo.
Bend-Portland Truck Service, Inc., Portland, Ore.
Briggs Transportation Company, St. Paul, Minn.
Bruce Motor Freight, Inc., Des Moines, Iowa
Burnside Motor Freight Lines, Inc., Urbana, Ohio
Callison Truck Lines, Inc., Eureka, California
Carolina-Norfolk Truck Line, Inc., Norfolk, Va.
Checker Express Company, Milwaukee, Wisc.
Chicago-Dubuque Motor Transport Co., Dubuque, Iowa
Churchill Truck Lines, Inc., Chillicothe, Mo.
Cochrane Transportation Company, Richmond, Va.
Columbus and Chicago Motor Freight, Inc., Columbus, Ohio
Commercial Motor Freight Inc., Columbus, Ohio
Commercial Motor Freight Inc. of Indiana, Indianapolis, Ind.
Cushman Motor Delivery Company, Chicago, Illinois
Days Transfer Inc., Elkhart, Ind.
Dohrn Transfer Company, Rock Island, Ill.
Duie A. Pyle, Inc., Coatesville, Pa.
Dundee Truck Lines, Inc., Toledo, Ohio
England Bros., Ft. Smith, Ark.
Expressways, Inc., Fort Wayne, Ind.
Georgia-Florida Motor Express, Inc., Jacksonville, Fla.
H. J. Tobler Transfer, Inc., Peru, Ill.
Hermann Forwarding Company, New Brunswick, N.J.
Hinchcliff Motor Service, Inc., Chicago, Ill.
Indianapolis & Southern Motor Express, Vincennes, Ind.
Jones Transfer, Rockford, Ill.
Jones Transfer Company, Monroe, Mich.
Leonard Bros. Motor Express Service, Inc., Greensburg, Pa.
McDaniel Freight Lines, Inc., Crawfordsville, Ind.
Masten Transportation, Inc., Milford, Dela.
Miami Transportation Company, Inc. of Indiana, Cincinnati, Ohio
Mid-American Truck Lines, Inc., Kansas City, Mo.
Moland Brothers Trucking Company, Duluth, Minn.
Motor Transport Company, Milwaukee, Wisc.
Mundy Motor Lines, Roanoke, Va.
Nenendorf Transportation Company, Inc., Madison, Wisc.

Nestor Bros., Inc., Endicott, N.Y.
New York and Worcester Express, Inc., New York, N.Y.
Newsour Trucking Company, Inc., Columbus, Ind.
Overnite Transportation Company, Richmond, Va.
Perkiomen Transfer, Inc., Allentown, Pa.
Ramus Trucking Line Company, Cleveland, Ohio
Red Ball Transfer Company, Omaha, Nebraska
Red Line, Inc., Roanoke, Va.
Rodgers Motor Lines, Inc., Scranton, Pa.
Royal Transit, Inc., Cleveland, Ohio
Royal Transportation Company, Bedford, Pa.
Salt Creek Freightways, Casper, Wyoming
Scannell E. J., Inc., Sommerville, Mass.
Security Cartage Company, Inc., Fort Wayne, Ind.
Smith and Soloman Trucking Co., New Brunswick, N.J.
Southern Express Company, Warren, Ohio
Stackpole, W. A., Motor Transportation, Inc., Manchester, N.H.
Standard Trucking Company, Charlotte, N.C.
Tennessee-Carolina Transportation, Inc., Nashville, Tenn.
Toedebusch Transfer Inc., St. Louis, Mo.
Transport Motor Express, Inc., Ft. Wayne, Ind.
Transportation Service, Inc., Detroit, Mich.
United Shipping Company, Minneapolis, Minn.
Valley Freight Lines, Inc., New Castle, Pa.
White Owl Express, Inc., Pontiac, Mich.
Wolleyhan Transport Company, Wilmington, Dela.
Wooster Express, Inc., Hartford, Conn.
Wright Trucking, Inc., Lowell, Mass.
Yankee Lines, Inc., Akron, Ohio

Chapter 2

The Optimal Use of Truck Fleets

A. VICTOR CABOT[1]
ARTHUR P. HURTER, JR.[1]

Introduction

The classic study by Koopmans in 1951 [14] was the first of a number of significant papers applying linear programming techniques to the problem of scheduling transportation equipment. A comprehensive bibliography of these works appears in a recent book by Ford and Fulkerson [9]. Many of the early papers were primarily attempts to construct mathematical models of real problems without regard for the availability of computational means for their solution. The more recent publications, on the other hand, are concerned with algorithms for the solution of these early problems. Recent attempts to solve the well-known "Traveling Salesman" problem by Dantzig [5] and Flood [8] are examples of this type of work.

This paper is concerned both with the formulation of a representative analytical model and its solution. This analytical formulation does not, however, result in a model of the classical network type. Instead, it is similar in many respects to the aircraft scheduling problem examined by Ferguson and Dantzig [4] since there is a great deal of attention paid to the role of the vehicle.

[1]Department of Industrial Engineering and Management Sciences and the Transportation Center, Northwestern University, Evanston, Illinois.

Two recent contributions to the literature which deal with a similar problem are also of note. One, a book by Ronald E. Miller [16], is also concerned with the application of linear programming to the scheduling of aircraft. In his monograph, Miller attempts to evaluate the efficiency of current airline practice. He does so by combining all airline companies into one large fictitious airline. He then derives the optimal schedule for this fictitious airline and compares it to the observed scheduling of the existing airlines. The other, by Robert F. Miller [15], gives a rather extensive coverage of the mathematical techniques involved in the analysis of problems concerned with scheduling. It includes a very comprehensive analysis of multi-equation systems.

This paper presents two scheduling models. One model is concerned with the problems faced by the operator of a private fleet of trucks. The operator must satisfy a given demand for his product, from given stocks, within a specified period of time, with a given truck fleet. Solution of this model yields a least cost schedule for the vehicles that will satisfy the requirements. The other model is concerned with scheduling problems faced by a common carrier. The carrier must deliver a given number of identified shipments, with a fixed number of vehicles, in a given period time. The model yields a schedule that will accomplish this with the smallest possible cost.

In addition, the paper develops a model that considers the interdependence between scheduling periods brought about through the use of a truck fleet of fixed size. The final portion of the paper considers the problem of computation for the multi-period model.

2.1 THE PRIVATE CARRIER

In this section, a model is developed to represent the scheduling problems facing the owner of a fleet of trucks. The method used considers some of the problems generally confronting the operator and tries to express them as realistically as possible in a mathematical format. While it is difficult to capture all the details of the physical situation, this procedure can capture the essence of the problem. For the most part, the operator of a private fleet of trucks is a part of a large organization built around the products to be distributed. The operator has at his disposal information concerning where the product is needed, how much of it is needed and how much is available for shipment at various locations. The operation may involve the distribution of goods from factories to warehouses, warehouses to stores, or even warehouses to warehouses. In any case, the operator knows the demands he must satisfy and the supply or capacity from which he must satisfy them. He is given, say on Friday night, the demands that must be satisfied by the following Friday night and his problem is to schedule his trucks over the week so as to meet those demands in the best possible way. We assume he uses a least cost criterion to determine the "best" schedule for the given demands and capacities. In many cases, the minimization of transport costs by the firm is not consistent with some other over-all firm objective such as profit maximization. For example, reduction in transport costs may lead to a loss of sales for the firm due to a reduced level of service. In this paper we shall ignore such interdependencies and assume that a minimization of cost is consistent with the firm's over-all objective, whatever it might be. We shall initially assume that the shipper has a certain number of vehicles available, each of the same capacity, and that this number cannot vary during the scheduling period. Later on, we shall consider the effect of a change in the size of the fleet on the optimum scheduling plan.

Since the operator knows the demands made upon him and the capacity or supply with which these demands are to be satisfied, the problem is quite similar to the standard transportation problem. For this reason, a linear programmimg model seems to be the best way to analyze the problem. The assumption of linearity may, in some cases, be considered to be an inadequate representation of the real situation. However, the traditional linear programming approach is so well developed that the information which can be gleaned from such a procedure *may* more than compensate for any misinterpretations due to some minor nonlinearities. In our problem, the only question of linearity involves the interpretation given to the costs to be minimized. If only line-haul costs are considered, then data prepared by the Interstate Commerce Commission [13] suggest that costs per vehicle mile may be considered constant for a given vehicle. In order to make the interpretations of the models as realistic as possible, however, it was necessary to include the terminal costs of unloading and loading each truck in the formulation of the cost function. The effect of this addition on the linearity of the system is discussed in the Appendix. We shall also assume that the routes to be taken between regions have been determined and will remain constant during the problem. By this we mean that the shortest or least cost route between Region A and Region B will be used to transport goods between the two points.

In the language of programming, the system under analysis consists of sources, those regions with goods to distribute, and sinks, regions that demand goods. A truck will depart from a source carrying a load to one of the sinks. Upon reaching the sink, it is possible for it to pick up another load and deliver it to another sink. This imparts a sort of transshipment characteristic to the sources and sinks, which we shall call nodes. Then, a node can be either a source or a sink at any time. It is possible for a node to have a demand but zero capacity and vice-versa. In this way, a consideration of empty backhauls is included. If a truck delivers to a node with zero capacity, it must travel empty to some other node which has capacity or else it must remain at the first node for the entire period.

To provide for as much realism as possible, the optimizing period is broken into a number of intervals. An interval will be defined as the length of time that it takes to go between the two closest locations. The other trips will be expressed as multiples of this basic interval. The number of intervals in the period will be determined by how many times the basic interval can be divided into the period. The length of a period will be determined by the time limits set on the meeting of demands. All shipments will start at the beginning of an interval. If the shipment is between two nodes that are one interval apart, the shipment is completed by the end of the interval. Shipments between nodes that are more than one interval apart will be assumed to be completed at the end of the interval during which they arrive. In other words, if it takes 1.5 intervals to go from A to B, then shipments from A to B are assumed to be completed at the end of the second interval. In short, to aid computations, the trips will be defined as integer multiples of the basic interval. Suppose the shortest trip possible took one day, while the others took various lengths of time up to three days. If all demands on the system are to be satisfied in one working week (five days), there are five shipping intervals in which to do all scheduling.

Deliveries may be made during any interval in the period. The only constraint on the shipments is that all demands must be satisfied by the end of the period. We also assume that each node-to-node movement has associated with it a fixed cost of shipping. That is, it costs a certain fixed amount to send a truck from node i to node j. The cost of a shipment (a loaded truck) from i to j is not necessarily the same as the cost of an empty truck making the same trip. The cost of sending a truckload from node i to node j is denoted C_{ij} and is defined as the sum of C'_{ij}, the cost of going from i to j and λ_j the terminal or unloading costs at node j,

$$(1) \quad C_{ij} = C'_{ij} + \lambda_j.$$

From this it can be seen that the cost of sending an empty truck will necessarily be less than sending a loaded truck as $\lambda_j = 0$ for an empty truck.

A formal statement of the constraints of the private carrier's problem may be written:

$$(2) \quad \sum_{t=1}^{T} \sum_{j=1}^{J} {}_pY_{ij}^t \leqq {}_pA_i, \quad i=1, \ldots, I, \ p=1, \ldots, P,$$

where ${}_pY_{ij}^t$ is the quantity in pounds of good p shipped from source i to sink j in interval t. ${}_pA_i$ is the total quantity of good p available at source i for shipping. The summation indicates that the shipments are distributed throughout the period from the first interval to the last (T-th).

Also

$$(3) \quad \sum_{t=1}^{T} \sum_{i=1}^{I} {}_pY_{ij}^t \geqq {}_pB_j, \quad j=1, \ldots, J, \ p=1, \ldots, P,$$

where ${}_pB_j$ is the total quantity of good p demanded at sink j during the period.

Further, we assume that the quantity available at all sources is at least as large as the quantity demanded at all sinks. That is:

$$\sum_{i=1}^{I} {}_pA_i \geqq \sum_{j=1}^{J} {}_pB_j,$$ which is assumed to hold for all p.

Let us assume that the capacity of each truck is K_p pounds for commodity p and, for simplicity, let us assume that all the commodities in the system have roughly the same shipping density. Then the capacity of one truck is K pounds. Now we may directly convert expressions (2) and (3) into terms of truckloads shipped by dividing through by the capacity, K, of one truck.

$$(4) \quad {}_pY_{ij}^t/K + {}_pf_{ij}^t = {}_pN_{ij}^t,$$

$$(5) \quad {}_pB_j/K + {}_pg_j = {}_pb_j,$$

$$p=1, \ldots, P, \ i=1, \ldots, I, \ j=1, \ldots, J, \ t=1, \ldots, T,$$

where ${}_pf_{ij}^t$ is the smallest fraction to be added to ${}_pY_{ij}^t/K$ to make it an integer ($_pf_{ij}^t \geqq 0$). Similarly, ${}_pg_j$ is the smallest fraction that must be added to ${}_pB_j/K$ to make the latter an integer ($_pg_j \geqq 0$). Now we may write expression (3) as:

$$(6) \quad \sum_{t=1}^{T} \sum_{i=1}^{I} {}_pN_{ij}^t \geqq {}_pb_j, \quad j=1, \ldots, J, \ p=1, \ldots, P,$$

where ${}_pb_j$ is an integer for all j, p. ${}_pN_{ij}^t$ is defined to be the number of trucks carrying commodity p going from source i to sink j in interval t. This number will always be an integer.

We must make an additional assumption in order to write expression (2) in terms of the ${}_pN_{ij}^t$ variables. We assume that all of the non-empty trucks leaving a source are filled to capacity except, perhaps, the last non-empty truck to leave. This in no way hinders the movement of empty trucks. It merely states that if a truck is loaded at all, it is full unless it is the last truck to leave the source with some load, in which case it might be partially loaded. This applies, of course, for each of the commodities to be shipped from the source. Thus if 50 trucks travel between A and B but only 30 loaded trucks are required to meet the demand at B, then 30 trucks are loaded, and 20 trucks are empty. Now we may write:

$$(7) \quad {}_pA_i/K + {}_ph_i = {}_pa_i, \quad p=1, \ldots, P, \; i=1, \ldots, I,$$

where ${}_pa_i$ is the largest integer number of trucks that can leave source i carrying good p, and ${}_ph_i$ is the fraction that must be added to ${}_pA_i/K$ to make the latter an integer (${}_ph_i \geq 0$). We now write expression (2) as:

$$(8) \quad \sum_{t=1}^{T} \sum_{j=1}^{J} {}_pN_{ij}^t \leq {}_pA_i, \; i=1, \ldots, I; \; p=1, \ldots, P \; .$$

The trucks initially will be dispersed among the several nodes. The total number of trucks in the system will be some constant and will be the sum of the number of trucks initially at each node:

$$(9) \quad \sum_{i=1}^{I} N_i^o = X.$$

At the end of the first interval the trucks will not be distributed in the same manner as they were at the start of the interval but certain restrictions must hold. The number of trucks leaving any source can never be greater than the number there at the beginning of the interval. In the first interval this number will be determined by the initial distribution, therefore,

$$(10) \quad \sum_{p=0}^{P} \sum_{j=1}^{J} {}_pN_{ij}^1 \leq N_i^o, \; i=1, \ldots, I.$$

Notice that p=0 denotes an empty truck.

After the first interval, the total number of trucks leaving a source must be less than the number which have come into it in previous intervals plus the number initially there. We may write a generalized expression:

$$(11) \quad \sum_{t=1}^{s} \sum_{p=0}^{P} \sum_{j=1}^{J} {}_pN_{ij}^t \leq \sum_{t=1}^{s-1} \sum_{p=0}^{P} \sum_{j=1}^{J} {}_pN_{ji}^t + N_i^o,$$

$$i=1, \ldots, I; \; s=2, \ldots, T,$$

for interval s. A slight modification of expression (11) puts it into traditional linear programming form:

$$(11)^* \quad \sum_{t=1}^{s} \sum_{p=0}^{P} \sum_{j=1}^{J} {}_pN_{ij}^t - \sum_{t=1}^{s-1} \sum_{p=0}^{P} \sum_{j=1}^{J} {}_pN_{ji}^t \leq N_i^o$$

This expression is true only if all nodes are one interval apart. If we examine two nodes A and B, which are two intervals apart, it is apparent that trucks leaving A bound for B in interval s-1 will not again be available until interval s+1. If it takes two intervals to go from A to B and one from A and B to all other nodes, we may write equation (11) for i=A as,

$$(12) \quad \sum_{t=1}^{s} \sum_{p=0}^{P} \sum_{j=1}^{J} {}_pN_{Aj}^t - \sum_{t=1}^{s-1} \sum_{p=0}^{P} \sum_{\substack{j=1 \\ j \neq B}}^{J} {}_pN_{jA}^t - \sum_{t=1}^{s-2} \sum_{p=0}^{P} {}_pN_{BA}^t \leq N_A^o,$$

$$s=3, \ldots, T.$$

When s=2, expression (11) will hold and trucks going from A to B will be considered unavailable. An analogous expression must be written for node B:

$$(13) \quad \sum_{t=1}^{s} \sum_{p=0}^{P} \sum_{j=1}^{J} {}_pN_{Bj}^t - \sum_{t=1}^{s-1} \sum_{p=0}^{P} \sum_{\substack{j=1 \\ j \neq A}}^{J} {}_pN_{jB}^t - \sum_{t=1}^{s-2} \sum_{p=0}^{P} {}_pN_{AB}^t \leq N_B^o$$

$$s=3, \ldots, T.$$

Since it takes two intervals to go from A to B, it is not possible to ship from A to B or from B to A in the last interval since the shipment would not arrive during the scheduling period in question. We must therefore include the additional restrictions:

$$(14) \quad \sum_{p=0}^{P} {}_pN_{AB}^T = 0,$$

and

$$(15) \quad \sum_{p=0}^{P} {}_pN_{BA}^T = 0.$$

If the cost of moving a truck from i to j varies with time, the problem facing the private carrier is:

(16) minimize $\sum\limits_{t=1}^{T} \sum\limits_{p=0}^{P} \sum\limits_{i=1}^{I} \sum\limits_{j=1}^{J} {}_pC_{ij}^t \, ({}_pN_{ij}^t)$,

subject to

(6) $\sum\limits_{t=1}^{T} \sum\limits_{i=1}^{I} {}_pN_{ij}^t \geqq {}_pb_j$, $\quad j=1, \ldots, J$, $p=1, \ldots, P$,

(8) $\sum\limits_{t=1}^{T} \sum\limits_{j=1}^{J} {}_pN_{ij} \leqq {}_pa_i$, $\quad i=1, \ldots, I$, $p=1, \ldots, P$,

and generally, for all nodes one interval apart,

(10) $\sum\limits_{p=0}^{P} \sum\limits_{j=1}^{J} {}_pN_{ij}^1 \leqq N_i^o$, $\quad i=1, \ldots, I$

and

(11) $\sum\limits_{t=1}^{s} \sum\limits_{p=0}^{P} \sum\limits_{j=1}^{J} {}_pN_{ij}^t - \sum\limits_{t=1}^{s-1} \sum\limits_{p=0}^{P} \sum\limits_{j=1}^{J} {}_pN_{ji}^t \leqq N_i^o$,

$\quad i=1, \ldots, I$, $s=2, \ldots, T$,

where

(17) ${}_pN_{ij}^t \geqq 0$ for all p,k,j,t and ${}_pN_{ij}^t$ an integer.

In the formulation of the model, represented by expressions (16), (6), (8), (10), (11), and (17), we have made use of two assumptions which warrant some additional discussion. We have assumed that the unit cost of moving a truck from i to j may vary with time. There are many possible justifications for this assumption. For example, deliveries early in the period help to insure that the demanding warehouses or stores do not suffer shortages in inventory or are in any other way hampered by poor delivery service. In this case the increasing cost is a premium the firm feels it should charge itself on "late" deliveries because goods are not available. Also we have assumed that if our model calls for 2.5 trucks of commodity p to be shipped from i to j and 1.5 trucks of commodity p + 1 to be shipped from i to j, we must send five trucks from i to j. We make no provision for mixing commodities in this model. In this way each "face" of our shipping tableau represents shipments for a separate commodity, unlike the three dimensional problem of Haley [11].

As in most linear programming problems, the dual of this problem provides economic insight. The dual of the problem stated in (16), (6), (8), (10), (11) and (17) is:

maximize:

$$(18) \quad \sum_{p=1}^{P} \sum_{j=1}^{J} (_pV_j)(_pb_j) - \sum_{p=1}^{P} \sum_{i=1}^{I} (_pa_i)(_pU_i) - \sum_{i=1}^{I} N_i^o \left(\sum_{t=1}^{T} w_i^t \right),$$

subject to:

$$(19) \quad _pV_j - {_pU_i} - \sum_{t=s}^{T} w_i^t + \sum_{t=s+1}^{T} w_j^t \leqq {_pC_{ij}^s}.$$

$$s=1, \ldots, T, \; i=1, \ldots, I, \; j=1, \ldots, J, \; p \; 1, \ldots, P,$$

$$(20) \quad -\sum_{t=s}^{T} w_i^t + \sum_{t=s+1}^{T} w_j^t \leqq {_pC_{ij}^s},$$

$$i=1, \ldots, I, \; j=1, \ldots, J, \; p=0, \; s=1, \ldots, T,$$

$$(21) \quad w_i^t, \; w_j^t, \; {_pU_i}, \; {_pV_j} \geqq 0 \text{ for all } i,j,t,p.$$

Expression (19) may be rewritten, in a form which aids interpretation, as:

$$(22) \quad _pV_j \leqq {_pU_i} + \sum_{t=s}^{T} w_i^t - \sum_{t=s+1}^{T} w_j^t + {_pC_{ij}^s},$$

for all p,i,j, $s=1, \ldots, T$.

$_pV_j$ may be interpreted as the value of good p unloaded at sink j. $_pU_i$ is the value of good p loaded onto a truck at source i. $_pC_{ij}^s$ is the per truck cost of sending a vehicle carrying good p from i to j in interval s and unloading it at j. The difference $\sum_{t=s}^{T} w_i^t - \sum_{t=s+1}^{T} w_j^t$ is the "rent" on the vehicle capacity foregone by sending a truck from i to j during the s-th interval.

The rent to truck capacity will be zero if the fleet at i is not used to capacity in interval s. The same will hold true for ensuing intervals when the truck is at j. If the fleet is used to capacity w_i^t may be interpreted as the amount the operator should be willing to pay to have one more truck available at source i at the beginning of interval t.

Expression (20) gives additional information. Suppose T=5 and a truck goes from i to j at s=3. Equation (20) would read:

$$(23) - [w_i^3 + w_i^4 + w_i^5] + w_j^4 + w_j^5 \leq {}_0C_{ij}^3.$$

We can interpret $w_i^3 + w_i^4 + w_i^5$ as the imputed value of the truck had it remained at i, and $w_j^4 + w_j^5$ as the imputed value of the truck at j during the subsequent intervals. If the vehicle remains at i, it will have to relinquish this imputed value at j, so the imputed

value of sending the truck to j is represented by $-\sum_{t=s}^{T} w_i^t + \sum_{t=s+1}^{T} w_j^t$.

As long as this difference is less than the cost of sending the truck to j ($_pC_{ij}^s$) the truck will remain at i. When the gain in rent value, $w_j^4 + w_j^5 - w_i^3 - w_i^4 - w_i^5$, is equal to the cost involved in sending the truck from i to j in interval 3, the truck is sent. The inequality cannot be reversed in an optimum solution since it would then be possible to increase (18) simply by moving empty trucks from i to j in the third interval.

The dual problem may be interpreted as the maximization of the difference between the delivered value of all of the truckloads of commodities and the sum of the value of the truckloads at the sources and the imputed value of the fleet capacity. The primal problem may be considered the minimization of direct costs of shipping. If we call the solution to the primal Z, and the solution to the dual Z*, we can combine the two problems into a "super" programming problem as shown by Dorfman, Samuelson, and Solow [7] and maximize the difference between the two, Z* - Z. Since at the optimum the value of the primal solution is equal to the value of the dual solution, the maximum value of this "super" problem will be zero. This difference between revenue less indirect costs and direct costs is the profit to the shipper. Thus, total profits on the shipping operation are zero. This is simply another way of saying that the values determined by the dual problem, the $_pV_j$, $_pU_i$, and w_i^t, are the prices that would be observed if freely competitive merchants purchased truckloads of goods at i for $_pU_i$, rented vehicles for w_i^t, shipped goods for $_pC_{ij}^t$ and sold goods for $_pV_j$. Put still another way, we can conceive of the firm as being divided into two decentralized divisions. One division, say A, produces commodities and attempts to satisfy demands by purchasing shipping services at final costs $_pC_{ij}^t$. Its objective is the minimization of shipping costs as given by (16). Division B behaves as an independent trucking firm, restricted to the commodities and demands and supplies of Division A. Division B purchases truckloads of goods from A for $_pU_i$, rents trucks for w_i^t, and sells truckloads of commodities for $_pV_j$. If the firm decided that it wanted to employ decentralized decision making, it should charge Division B prices $_pU_i$ and w_i^t and tell it to maximize its profits. This is essentially what expression (18) says. This will lead the manager of Division B to an optimal shipping schedule.

The primal problem is suggestive of the similarity of the private carrier's model and the standard transportation problem. The dual problem bears a close resemblance to the capacitated transportation problem with the capacities placed on the sources and not on the branches connecting the nodes. A favored basis for the primal problem could be selected, following the double-reverse technique of Charnes and Cooper [2]. The resulting "favored" problem can be solved using a transportation algorithm. Then, by adding the additional constraints and checking their effect on the basis, we might be able to solve the larger problem generated by our model. For large problems, however, especially those involving many intervals, this would probably involve as much or more work than solving the entire problem directly. There is one constraint for each node in each time interval. For a problem with m+n nodes and T intervals, an additional (T)(m+n) constraints must be tested when the basis of the favored problem involved only [2 (m+n)-1](P) constraints.

A sample problem for private carriers was solved on the IBM 709 digital computer. The code was a C-E-I-R program, LP 90, which not only gave the optimal solution, but performed parametric programming on requirements and costs. The problem, as will be seen following, appears to be a very simple one and yet it took the computer six minutes to obtain an optimal solution. The private carrier in the sample problem has three locations to serve. Each has both capacity to distribute and demands to satisfy. In the problem we shall assume that capacity exceeds demand.

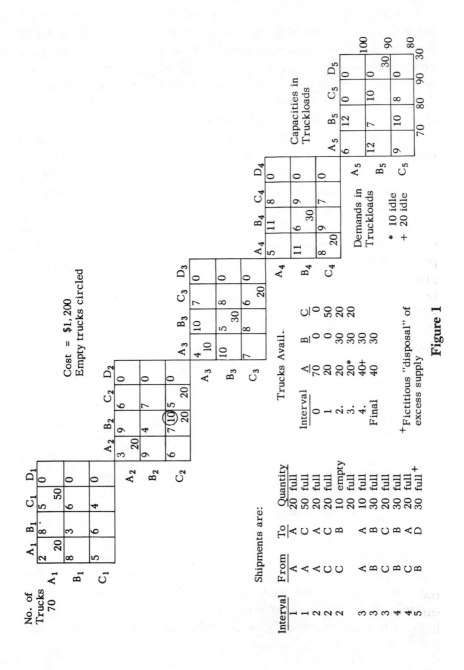

Figure 1

All nodes with the exception of A and B are one interval apart. It takes two intervals to go from A to B. Each node is divided into a source and a sink and it is possible to ship from the source of a node to the sink of the same node. A shipment of this type takes one interval. The cost associated with such a shipment contains both the shipping and back-haul costs.

As previously mentioned, the shipping costs for loaded trucks increase with time while the shipping costs for empty trucks remain constant, i.e., $_0C^1_{12} = {}_0C^2_{12}$, and $_0C^1_{12} = {}_1C^1_{12} < {}_1C^2_{12}$. The sample problem considers only one commodity and all the shipper's trucks are assumed to be initially centered at source A. The demands, as indicated in figure 1, are A = 70, B = 80, C = 90 and D = 30 (where D is a dummy sink) and capacities are A = 100, B = 90, C = 80. There are seventy trucks at source A to start the period. In this problem, trucks may go from any source to any sink imparting a transshipment characteristic to the nodes, but there has been no provision made for the transshipment of goods.

The total cost of the schedule is $1,200 and the operator must send ten empty trucks from C to B in the second interval to achieve this optimal solution. It is interesting to notice that the shipper does not send any trucks directly from A to B. Since they are two intervals apart, a shipment between the two would not only be of a high direct cost but would keep trucks out of the system for two intervals. The final distribution of trucks is 40 trucks at A, 30 at B and no trucks at C. This is the distribution with which the shipper will start the next period. The importance of the initial distribution of trucks will be considered at length in a later section of the paper.

2.2 THE COMMON CARRIER

The common carrier's freight consists of packages which must be distributed among the sinks as prescribed by the consignor. There is no demand for the packages at the sink, only the specification that the package be carried from the i-th source to the j-th sink. The problem confronting the common carrier is similar to the private carrier's in that he must deploy his trucks in such a way as to minimize his costs.

If we take all the shipments bound from a particular source to a particular sink we may obtain, by methods previously used in examining the private carrier's problem, the minimum number of trucks which can carry the goods of one source to one sink. Let A_{ij} be equal to the number of pounds of good going from i to j. Again letting K be the capacity of one truck, we have:

$$(24) \quad A_{ij}/K + f_{ij} = a_{ij}.$$

Here, a_{ij} is the number of loaded trucks that must go from i to j, if all but the last truck are fully loaded. In this case, f_{ij} is that amount added to A_{ij}/K to make it an integer ($f_{ij} \geqq 0$). So we have an expression,

$$(25) \quad \sum_{t=1}^{T} {}_pN_{ij}^t = a_{ij}, \text{ where } p = 1 \text{ for all i,j,}$$

with p=1 signifying that the truck is loaded. The constraints on the truck fleet itself are exactly the same as those for the private carrier with the exception that a truck may carry many commodities, since each package is labeled. The initial distribution of trucks once again plays a major role in the scheduling. For the first interval,

$$(26) \quad \sum_{p=0}^{1} \sum_{j=1}^{J} {}_pN_{ij}^t \leqq N_i^o, \quad i=1, \ldots, I,$$

where p=0 for an empty truck and p=1 for a loaded truck, and

$$(27) \quad \sum_{t=1}^{s} \sum_{p=0}^{1} \sum_{j=1}^{J} {}_pN_{ij}^t - \sum_{t=1}^{s-1} \sum_{p=0}^{1} \sum_{j=1}^{J} {}_pN_{ji}^t \leqq N_i^o,$$
$$i=1, \ldots, I, s=2, \ldots, T.$$

This expression assumes all nodes to be one interval apart. It may be varied to fit the characteristics of the problem. Expression (25) assumes that the carrier has the entire period to make the indicated deliveries. In this case, the costs to the operator may also be thought of as varying with time. The rationale behind this assumption is the natural wish of consignees to get their merchandise as quickly as possible. For failing to meet these wishes, the carrier suffers a loss in "good will" for which he should "charge" himself. In the case of the common carrier we must include the cost of loading the vehicle,

61

say at source i, γ_i, and of unloading it at sink j, λ_j, in the direct costs of transportation along with the point-to-point costs C'_{ij}. Therefore,

(28) $C_{ij} = C'_{ij} + \gamma_i + \lambda_j$.

This differs from our treatment of costs in the private carrier problem, since in the latter case loading costs were included with other costs of production.

The problem of the common carrier may be stated as follows:

(29) minimize $\displaystyle\sum_{t=1}^{T} \sum_{p=0}^{1} \sum_{i=1}^{I} \sum_{j=1}^{J} {}_pC^t_{ij} \, ({}_pN^t_{ij})$,

subject to

(25) $\displaystyle\sum_{t=1}^{T} {}_pN^t_{ij} = a_{ij}$ for all i,j, p=1,

(26) $\displaystyle\sum_{p=0}^{1} \sum_{j=1}^{J} {}_pN^1_{ij} \leqq N^o_i$, i=1, . . . , I,

(27) $\displaystyle\sum_{t=1}^{S} \sum_{p=0}^{1} \sum_{j=1}^{J} {}_pN^t_{ij} - \sum_{t=1}^{s-1} \sum_{p=0}^{1} \sum_{j=1}^{J} {}_pN^t_{ji} \leqq N^o_i$,

i=1, . . . , I, s=2, . . . , T,

(30) ~~$_pN^t_{ij} \geqq 0$ for all i,j,t,p, $_pN^t_{ij}$ an integer.~~

The carrier wants to minimize his costs over the total period while still delivering all the shipments and not violating the physical restrictions placed on him by his fleet.

The dual problem may be written

(31) maximize $\displaystyle\sum_{i=1}^{I} \sum_{j=1}^{J} (a_{ij}) (U_{ij}) - \sum_{t=1}^{T} \sum_{i=1}^{I} (N^o_i) (w^t_i)$,

subject to:

(32) $U_{ij} - \displaystyle\sum_{t=s}^{T} w^t_i + \sum_{t=s+1}^{T} w^t_j \leqq {}_pC^x_{ij}$,

s=1, . . . , T, i=1, . . . , I, j=1, . . . , J, p=1,

(33) $-\displaystyle\sum_{t=s}^{T} w^t_i + \sum_{t=s+1}^{T} w^t_j \leqq C^x_{ij}$,

p=0, s=1, . . . , T, j=1, . ., J, i=1, . . . , I , and

(34) $w^t_i, \ w^t_j, \ \geqq 0$ for all i, j, t.

Expression (32) can be rewritten as:

$$(35) \quad U_{ij} \leqq \sum_{t=s}^{T} w_i^t - \sum_{t=s+1}^{T} w_j^t + {}_pC_{ij}^s,$$

$$s=1, \ldots, T, \; i=1, \ldots, J, \; j=1, \ldots, J, \; p=1.$$

Here we again interpret w_i^t as the rent to truck capacity and ${}_pC_{ij}^s$ as the cost to the carrier for supplying transportation. U_{ij} may be interpreted as the rate that a purely competitive trucker, with a constraint on the vehicles available to him, would charge for a full truckload from i to j. The imputed value of a truck at i in interval s is $w_{\cdot i}^s$. If it goes to j in this interval its value will be $w_j^{s+1} + w_j^{s+2} + \ldots + w_j^T$. This is the rent the truck will "gain" by going to j. The carrier will send a truck from i to j only when the imputed value of the truck plus the transportation cost is equal to the rate from i to j. If it is greater than the rate the operator will not send the vehicle. If the carriers operated in pure competition, it would be impossible for the rate charged from i to j to be greater than the sum of the truck "rents" and the cost per truck in going from i to j including "normal" profit. If a trucker were to charge a higher rate, competitors would instantly enter the market charging a slightly lower rate and the first trucker would find it necessary to lower his rate to meet the competition. The market equilibrium condition requires that the actual rate charged by the carrier be equal to the U_{ij} determined by the model. Where actual rates are not competitively determined, there is no guarantee of their equality with the U_{ij}.

In fact, if rates are completely regulated, the common carrier in our problem knows what his total revenue will be as soon as he knows what shipments he must carry over the time period of interest. Thus, where rates are regulated and shipments designated for the carrier, minimizing the cost of making the shipments is equivalent to maximizing the carrier's profit. Equation (33) is the same as equation (20) in the private carrier's model and may be interpreted in the same way.

The dual of the common carrier's problem may be interpreted, in pure competition, as the maximization of the difference between total revenue and indirect truck capacity rent subject to the constraint that

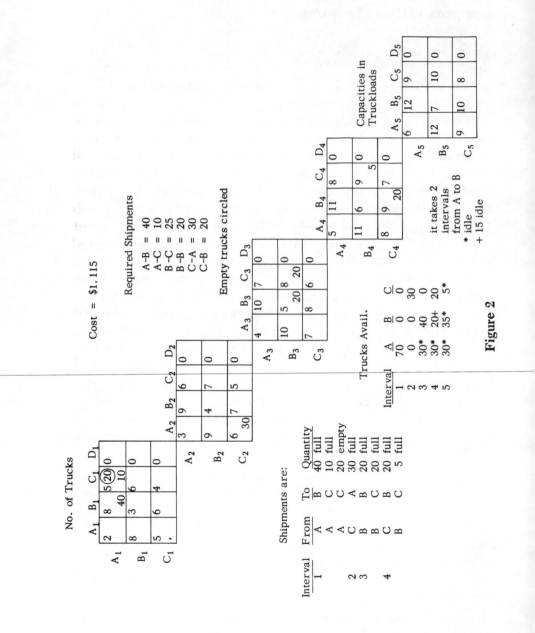

Figure 2

unit profit not exceed zero. The primal problem may be considered the minimization of direct costs constrained by the fleet capacity.

Figure 2 is a sample problem worked out for the common or for-hire carrier. The costs are the same as in the example for the private carrier and are similarly assumed to increase with time. The costs of moving empty trucks are assumed to remain the same in all intervals. The geography is assumed to be the same as that used in the private carrier's problem, with all nodes one interval apart with the exception of A and B which are two intervals apart. The initial distribution of trucks was the same with seventy at A and zero at B and C. Requirements are indicated and total scheduling cost is $1,115. In the first interval the only allocation of empty trucks takes place with 20 trucks going form A to C. It might be of interest to note that since a direct shipment from A to B was required it took place in the first interval thus freeing the trucks at B in the third interval for shipments elsewhere.

2.3 SIMULTANEOUS USE OF PRIVATE AND FOR-HIRE TRUCKING

Suppose that the private trucker feels that certain advantages could be gained from using a mixture of common and for-hire carriage. For example, he may feel that he can reduce his total transport costs by using his own trucks for short trips and by using for-hire carriers for longer trips. This added flexibility for the shipper requires that the private carrier model be modified.

Including the possibility of using for-hire carriers does not alter the vehicle capacity constraints of the shipper's private fleet. As far as this single shipper is concerned, the for-hire carrier is considered a true common carrier and no constraint on the number of for-hire vehicles available is considered. We shall write $_pF_{ij}^t$ as the number of truckloads of good p being carried for our shipper by for-hire trucks from i to j in the t-th interval. Then, the modified private carrier's problem becomes:

$$(36) \quad \text{minimize} \sum_{t=1}^{T} \sum_{p=0}^{P} \sum_{i=1}^{I} \sum_{j=1}^{J} [_pC_{ij}^t \ (_pN_{ij}^t) \ + d_{ij}^t \ (_pF_{ij}^t)]$$

Where d^t_{ij} is the cost per truckload, to the shipper, of using for-hire trucking from i to j in interval t. The minimization is subject to:

$$(37) \quad \sum_{t=1}^{T} \sum_{j=1}^{J} ({}_pN^t_{ij} + {}_pF^t_{ij}) \leqq {}_pa_i, \quad i=1, \ldots, I, \; p=1, \ldots, P,$$

$$(38) \quad \sum_{t=1}^{T} \sum_{i=1}^{I} ({}_pN^t_{ij} + {}_pF^t_{ij}) \geqq {}_pb_j, \quad j=1, \ldots, J, \; p=1, \ldots, P,$$

$$(39) \quad \sum_{p=0}^{P} \sum_{j=1}^{J} {}_pN^1_{ij} \leqq N^o_i, \quad i=1, \ldots, I$$

$$(40) \quad \sum_{t=1}^{s} \sum_{p=0}^{P} \sum_{j=1}^{J} {}_pN^t_{ij} - \sum_{t=1}^{s-1} \sum_{p=0}^{P} \sum_{j=1}^{J} {}_pN^t_{ji} \leqq N^o_i$$

$$i=1, \ldots, I, \; s=2, \ldots, T,$$

$(41) \quad {}_pN^t_{ij}, \; {}_pF^t_{ij} \geqq 0$, for all i,j,p,t and ${}_pN^t_{ij}$ an integer.

Equation (36) involves an assumption that cannot ordinarily be justified by reference to empirical fact. Since ${}_pF^t_{ij}$ is not required to be an integer, we have tacitly assumed that the rate d^t_{ij} per unit weight (truckload) is the same whether or not full truckloads are shipped. In other words, we have ignored any differences between T.L. and L.T.L. rates. Conceptually, it is not difficult to include a consideration of these rate differences. It merely requires that we identify whether or not a shipment is T.L. or L.T.L. Equation (36) would be modified to:

$$\text{minimize} \sum_t \sum_p \sum_i \sum_j [{}_pC^t_{ij} \; ({}_pN^t_{ij}) + d^t_{ij} ({}_pF^t_{ij}) + d^{t'}_{ij} ({}_pF^{t'}_{ij})]$$

Where $d^{t'}_{ij}$ is the L.T.L. rate and d^t_{ij} is the T.L. rate. This kind of modification can be extended to include other modes of transport as well. However, while these modifications are not difficult on a conceptual level, the data requirements and computational problems very rapidly become intractable. For purposes of further exposition in this paper, we restrict our attention to the model defined by expressions (36), (37), (38), (39), (40), and (41).

The dual of the stated problem is:

(42) maximize

$$\sum_{p=1}^{P} \sum_{j=1}^{J} (_pb_j)(_pV_j) - \sum_{p=1}^{P} \sum_{i=1}^{I} (_pA_i)(_pU_i) - \sum_{i=1}^{I} N_i^o \left[\sum_{t=1}^{T} w_i^t \right]$$

subject to

(43) $\displaystyle _pV_j - _pU_i - \sum_{t=s}^{T} w_i^t + \sum_{t=s+1}^{T} w_j^t \leqq {}_pC_{ij}^s$

$p=1, \ldots, P, s=1, \ldots, T$ and all i,j

(44) $_pV_j - _pU_i \leqq d_{ij}^t$

$p=1, \ldots, P, i=1, \ldots, I, j=1, \ldots, J, t=1, \ldots, T$

(45) $\displaystyle -\sum_{t=s}^{T} w_i^t + \sum_{t=s+1}^{T} w_j^t \leqq {}_pC_{ij}^s$ all i,j,s=1, \ldots, T, p=0

(46) $w_i^t, w_j^t, {}_pU_i, {}_pV_j \geqq 0$ for all i,j,t,p.

Expression (43) represents the typical private carrier's constraint stating that marginal profit on the shipping activity be no greater than zero. It is exactly analagous to expression (19). Again, $_pV_j$ is the delivered value of commodity p at sink j, $_pU_i$ the price of p on the truck at source i and w_i^t and w_j^t the imputed value to truck capacity at source i and sink j respectively in interval t. On the other hand equation (44) does not contain any terms for rents to truck capacity. The price of for-hire carriage d_{ij}^t is given and a shipment will be sent when the delivered value of good p is equal to the price of the good on the truck plus the transportation cost. Notice that there is no constraint pertaining to the movement of empty trucks for the for-hire carrier similar to (45) for the private carrier. The availability of for-hire shipping is not limited and therefore no dual variable exists for it.

2.4 THE SCHEDULING OF DRIVERS AND OF MAINTE-NANCE

Thus far, the paper has had nothing to say about the scheduling of drivers, the scheduling of maintenance, or the scheduling of special hauls for the private carrier. These considerations add many complications which may require major modifications in the preceding analytical representation of the truck scheduling problem. These complications do exist, however, and any attempt at scheduling cannot completely disregard them. Certain trucks, for example, may be required to finish the scheduling period at a certain node at which there are maintenance facilities. It may be that trucks can be "on the road" for no longer than a specified number of intervals (days) in succession due to driver commitments. The firms may have several trucks of a certain desirable type available for transporting a special product (e.g., refrigerated trucks) and these trucks may not be used, or are inefficiently used, if they are employed without concern for their special advantages.

To develop a model for private carrier scheduling with these complications accounted for, we shall have to identify each truck. Consider the trucks numbered from one to X, the number of trucks available. Initially, the trucks will be distributed throughout the system of nodes. We shall identify the r-th truck by a superscript so $^rN_i^o$ is a variable that takes on values of 1 or 0 depending upon whether or not the r-th truck is or is not initially located at node i.

Clearly, $\sum_{i=1}^{I} \,^rN_i^o = 1$ for each r.

Therefore,

$$(47) \quad \sum_{r=1}^{X} \sum_{i=1}^{I} \,^rN_i^o = X,$$

where,

$$(48) \quad ^rN_i^o = \begin{cases} 0 \\ 1 \end{cases} \text{ if r-th truck } \begin{smallmatrix} \text{is not} \\ \text{is} \end{smallmatrix} \text{ initially at i. With this modifi-}$$

cation in the nature of variables to be determined, the formal structure of the private carrier model discussed earlier can be applied.

$$(49) \quad \text{minimize} \quad \sum_{t=1}^{T} \sum_{r=1}^{X} \sum_{i=1}^{I} \sum_{j=1}^{J} \sum_{p=0}^{P} (_pC_{ij}^t) \, (_p^rN_{ij}^t)$$

subject to:

$$(50) \quad \sum_{t=1}^{T} \sum_{r=1}^{X} \sum_{j=1}^{J} {}_{p}^{r}N_{ij}^{t} \leqq {}_{p}a_{i}, \quad i=1, \ldots, I, \ p=1, \ldots, P,$$

$$(51) \quad \sum_{t=1}^{T} \sum_{r=1}^{X} \sum_{i=1}^{I} {}_{p}^{r}N_{ij}^{t} \geqq {}_{p}b_{j}, \quad j=1, \ldots, J, \ p=1, \ldots, P,$$

$$(52) \quad \sum_{r=1}^{X} \sum_{j=1}^{J} \sum_{p=0}^{P} {}_{p}^{r}N_{ij}^{1} \leqq N_{i}^{o}, \quad i=1, \ldots, I,$$

$$(53) \quad \sum_{t=1}^{s} \sum_{r=1}^{X} \sum_{p=0}^{P} \sum_{j=1}^{J} {}_{p}^{r}N_{ij}^{t} - \sum_{t=1}^{s-1} \sum_{r=1}^{X} \sum_{p=0}^{P} \sum_{j=1}^{J} {}_{p}^{r}N_{ji}^{t} \leqq N_{i}^{o}$$

$$i=1, \ldots, I, \ s=2, \ldots, T,$$

$$(54) \quad \text{where} \quad {}_{p}^{r}N_{ij}^{t} = \begin{Bmatrix} 0 \\ 1 \end{Bmatrix} \text{ for all } i,j,t,p,r.$$

We can solve this as an integer programming problem with a variable for each i,j,t,p and r by substituting for (54)

$$(55) \quad {}_{p}^{r}N_{ij}^{t} \geqq 0,$$

and   for all i,j,t,r,p.

$$(56) \quad {}_{p}^{r}N_{ij}^{t} \leqq 1.$$

Since there is a variable for every subscript and superscript, a problem with a large fleet of trucks and many nodes will have a great many variables indeed. However, this model provides for a great deal of the flexibility in the kinds of constraints considered. For example, suppose that some truck "r" must be in sink B at the end of the period for servicing. This can be achieved very simply by adding the restriction

$$(57) \quad \sum_{i=1}^{I} \sum_{p=0}^{P} {}_{p}^{r}N_{iB}^{T} = 1.$$

The r-th truck must go to B in the final interval carrying any commodity or going empty.

While equation (57) was used to insure that truck r goes to node B in T, similar restrictions imposed on the fleet could in fact send any truck to any source in any interval. This general procedure is applicable to the common carrier model as well.

2.5 THE INTERSCHEDULING PERIOD INFLUENCE OF INITIAL TRUCK DISTRIBUTIONS

In most problems, the initial distribution of trucks does much to determine the cost for the period. There may exist some initial distribution of trucks which, for given demands and capacities, will always give a lower cost than other initial distributions.

If the trucker knew that his demands were going to be the same for each period for some time in the future and if he also knew the optimal initial distribution of trucks in each period, it might be possible for him to constrain the trucks in the first period in such a manner that they were optimally distributed for the next period. This could result in additional costs in the first period but a minimum cost over the several periods.

In the following examples we demonstrate that, given a series of scheduling tableaus with the same or approximately the same demands and capacities, the final distribution of trucks in each period may approach the initial distribution of that period. When this is the case, the costs will be approximately the same for successive periods. If it were true that this "steady state" distribution of trucks were the lowest cost distribution that could be obtained with the given initial distribution of trucks in the first period, it might be an advantage to constrain the allocation of trucks, at the end of the first period, to this "steady state" distribution.

The example graphed in Figure 3 illustrates the case just discussed. After the third period, if the requirements are left unchanged, the distribution becomes stabilized at a minimum per period cost of $1,110. In period two, however, the cost reached a low of $1,080. The first period computation is illustrated in Figure 1, the second and third by Figures 4 and 5 respectively.

Since the second period's initial distribution of trucks results in the lowest cost, it would be foolish to constrain the trucks in the first period to yield any distribution of trucks other than the one that results from the cost minimization. If the distribution of trucks in the second period were constrained to the same distribution at the end of the interval as at the beginning, it is possible that the over-all sever-

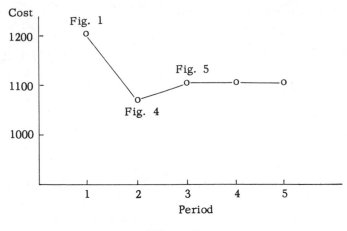

Figure 3

al periods costs may be reduced despite the presence of an additional constraint. Figure 7 reveals that the cost of scheduling the fleet to satisfy requirements and to finish each period with the same intial distribution of trucks as period two, is $1,200. This is much more than the $1,110 of period three. Figure 6 shows that the shipper achieves the least total costs by letting the system be optimized in each period.

We are not justified in generalizing this result for all cases. It could be that the cost associated with constraining the trucks might not be so substantial in other examples and in these cases a real savings might be achieved by this simple technique. For example, consider a case where the costs took a particularly long time to level off. The trucker might impose an "optimal" initial distribution for future periods as the final distribution of trucks in the first period. In this way he might achieve lower costs and ease his scheduling chores at the same time.

On Figure 8, plan B is the natural path that scheduling might follow over several periods given the initial distribution and using single period cost minimization techniques. A cost reduction might be induced by using Plan A which has higher cost in the first period due to additional constraints but settles immediately to a lower cost

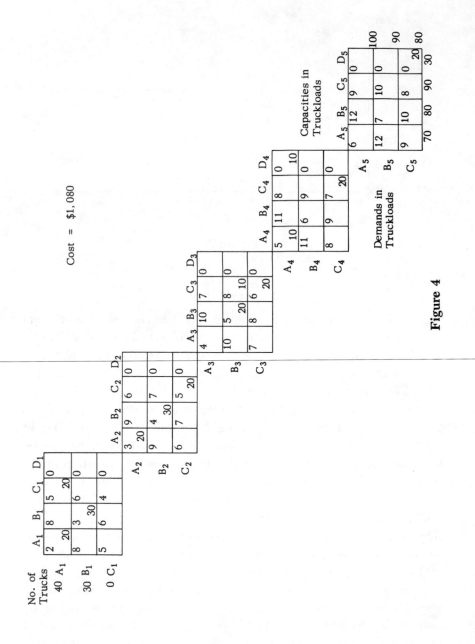

Figure 4

THE OPTIMAL USE OF TRUCK FLEETS

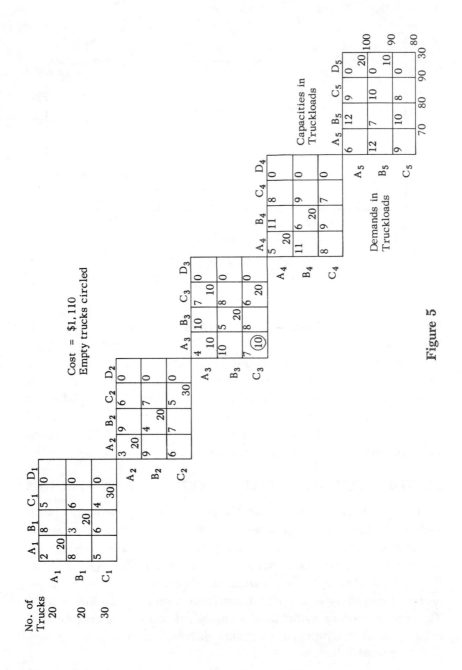

Figure 5

73

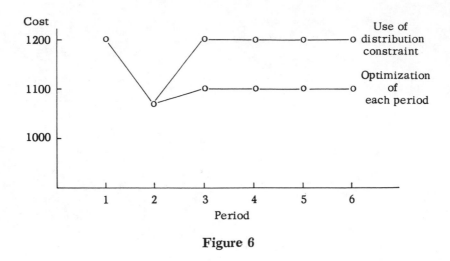

Figure 6

for several periods. Eventually, the cost of B equals the cost of A. Notice that additional constraints on final truck distribution are required, in Plan A, *only* for the first period. It is quite possible that the operator might want to control the distribution of trucks for some reason other than to minimize his costs. The scheduling of drivers could be a reason for wanting no more than a certain fixed number of trucks at any source at the end of the period. These problems are discussed at length in section 2.9.

2.6 THE OPTIMAL INITIAL DISTRIBUTION OF TRUCKS

Thus far we have assumed that the private fleet operator was faced with a scheduling problem constrained by a given initial geographic distribution of his fleet. In this section, we consider a modified problem in which the operator determines the initial distribution of his fleet as well as an optimal schedule. In the previous section we demonstrated the effect of the initial distribution on the scheduling costs. The private carrier's model may be modified so that the cost minimization process determines the optimal distribution of vehicles as well as the optimal schedule.

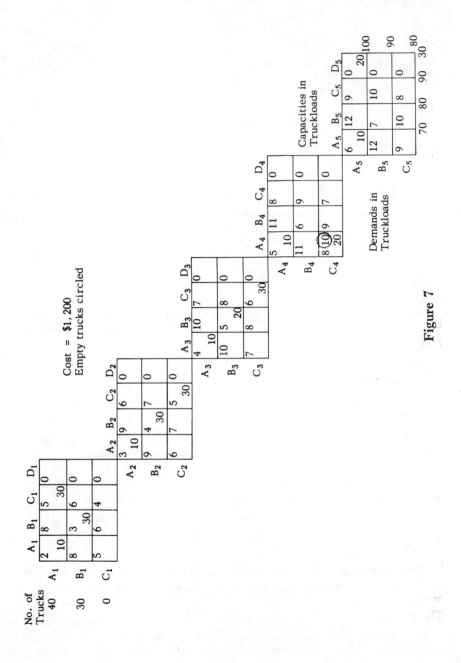

Figure 7

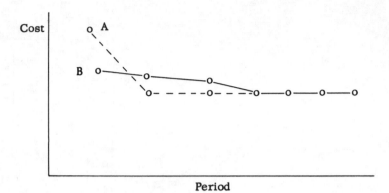

Figure 8

The private carrier's model, depicted in expressions (16), (6), (8), (10) and (11), can be modified to include expressions (58) and (59) in place of (10) and (11), where:

$$(58) \quad \sum_{p=0}^{P} \sum_{j=1}^{J} {}_{p}N_{ij}^{1} - {}_{p}N_{i}^{o} \leqq 0, \quad i=1, \ldots, I, \text{ and}$$

$$(59) \quad \sum_{t=1}^{s} \sum_{p=0}^{P} \sum_{j=1}^{J} {}_{p}N_{ij}^{t} - \sum_{t=1}^{s-1} \sum_{p=0}^{P} \sum_{j=1}^{J} {}_{p}N_{ji}^{t} - N_{i}^{o} \leqq 0,$$

$$i=1, \ldots, I, s=2, \ldots, T.$$

In other words, the number of trucks leaving any source must be less than the number that have entered previously plus the number there initially. This is the same interpretation given earlier, *except that now the* N_{i}^{o} *are treated as variables.*

We continue to assume that the private operator has a fixed number of vehicles, X, at his disposal for the coming period. Or, as previously stated,

$$(9) \quad \sum_{i=1}^{I} N_{i}^{o} = X.$$

A full statement of the modified problem is:

$$(60) \quad \text{minimize} \sum_{t=1}^{T} \sum_{p=0}^{P} \sum_{i=1}^{I} \sum_{j=1}^{J} {}_{p}C_{ij}^{t} \, ({}_{p}N_{ij}^{t}) + \sum_{i=1}^{I} (0) \, N_{i}^{o}$$

subject to:

$$(6) \quad \sum_{t=1}^{T} \sum_{i=1}^{I} {}_{p}N_{ij}^{t} \geqq {}_{p}b_{j}, \qquad \begin{matrix} j=1, \ldots, J \\ p=1, \ldots, P \end{matrix}$$

$$(8) \quad \sum_{t=1}^{T} \sum_{j=1}^{J} {}_{p}N_{ij}^{t} \leqq {}_{p}a_{i}, \qquad \begin{matrix} i=1, \ldots, I, \\ p=1, \ldots, P \end{matrix}$$

$$(58) \quad \sum_{p=0}^{P} \sum_{j=1}^{J} {}_{p}N_{ij}^{1} - N_{i}^{o} \leqq 0 \qquad i=1, \ldots, I$$

$$(59) \quad \sum_{t=1}^{s} \sum_{p=0}^{P} \sum_{j=1}^{J} {}_{p}N_{ij}^{t} - \sum_{t=1}^{s-1} \sum_{p=0}^{P} \sum_{j=1}^{J} {}_{p}N_{ji}^{t} - N_{i}^{o} \leqq 0$$

$$i=1, \ldots, I, s=2, \ldots, T$$

$$(9) \quad \sum_{i=1}^{I} N_{i}^{o} = X$$

where

$$(61) \quad {}_{p}N_{ij}^{t}, \quad N_{i}^{o} \geqq 0 \text{ and an integer for all } i,j,p,t.$$

Expression (60) indicates that the N_{i}^{o} are now to be treated as variables. Each of these variables is multipled by zero in the criterion function, indicating that the operator has no cost associated with his choice of an initial distribution. In this case, the private carrier operator can have his vehicles delivered to any geographic location at the beginning of the scheduling period at no charge. This will not, of course, always be true. There will often be some positive cost associated with each possible initial distribution. In this case the coefficients of the N_{i}^{o} in the criterion function would not all be zero. This alteration makes no formal difference in the model and therefore for purposes of exposition we shall return to the "no charge" situation indicated in expression (60).

THE OPTIMAL USE OF TRUCK FLEETS

The dual of the problem stated above is:

$$(62) \quad \text{maximize} \sum_{p=1}^{P} \sum_{i=1}^{I} (_pV_j)(_pb_j) - \sum_{p=1}^{P} \sum_{i=1}^{I} (_pa_i)(_pU_i) - (y)X$$

subject to:

$$(19) \quad _pV_j - {_pU_i} - \sum_{t=s}^{T} w_i^t + \sum_{t=s+1}^{T} w_j^t \leqq {_pC_{ij}^s}$$

$$s=1, \ldots, T, \ i=1, \ldots, I, \ j=1, \ldots, J, \ p=1, \ldots, P$$

$$(20) \quad -\sum_{t=s}^{T} w_i^t + \sum_{t=s+1}^{T} w_j^t \leqq {_0C_{ij}^s}$$

$$i=1, \ldots, I, \ j=1, \ldots, J, \ s=1, \ldots, T,$$

$$(63) \quad \sum_{t=1}^{T} w_i^t - y \leqq 0$$

$$i=1, \ldots, I,$$

where

$$(64) \quad w_j^t, \ w_j^t, \ _pU_i, \ _pV_j, \ y \geqq 0 \text{ for all } i,j,t,p.$$

Here, the dual has essentially the same interpretation as it had in the original problem. An added feature included in the dual problem stated above is the imputed value of the truck fleet itself. The criterion function, expression (62), states that the difference between the delivered value of the good and the sum of the value of the good on the truck and the rent to the fleet of trucks is to be maximized.

Expression (63) may be rewritten:

$$(65) \quad \sum_{t=1}^{T} w_i^t \leqq y, \ i=1, \ldots, I,$$

which indicates that the total imputed value to the trucks at any source, throughout the period, cannot exceed the imputed value of the fleet.

In the numerical example which follows we have taken the same demands and supplies that were present in the preceding examples

78

but made the number of trucks initially at each source a variable. We achieve, as expected, a lower cost than in previous examples and the initial distribution of thirty trucks at A, twenty at B and at C. This is the optimal initial distribution of trucks since it yields the lowest cost, $1,050. Notice that this initial distribution does not repeat itself. The final vehicle distribution, as shown by Figure 9, is 30 at A, 20 at B and 20 at C.

2.7 "ECONOMIES OF SCALE"

Economies of scale are said to occur when the firm with larger physical capacity begins to enjoy a marked advantage over its smaller brother in the unit cost of its operations. This advantage may be brought about by mass production, easier planning, or any number of things which are made available to it by virtue of its larger size [12].

There are varying points of view when it comes to the subject of "economies of scale" in the trucking industry. In his paper on the subject, Stanley Warner [22] states, "The study does suggest that any *given* physical set of shipments is apt to be carried more cheaply by a combined firm than by a number of firms." He also states, however,

> Certainly the economies suggested are not overpowering in the sense that such differences as there are cannot be overcome by a favorably situated small firm. The main determinant of profitability in the trucking business is the nature of the collection of shipments that a firm is lucky or unlucky enough to be in line for.

It will be our objective to ascertain any scheduling advantages the larger fleet owner may have over several smaller ones.

If we divide each of the demands and capacities of the problem depicted in Figure 4 by two and divide the initial distribution of trucks by two, we will obtain a smaller scheduling problem which is that of a firm exactly one half the size of the one referred to in Figure 4. Since the costs used in Figure 4 are costs per truck there is no reason to change these. It will cost the same for a small operator to send his truck (the same size as the larger operator's truck) from any i to any j.

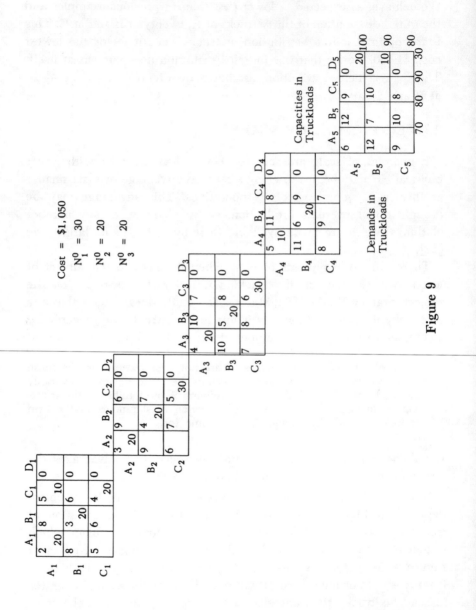

Cost = $1,050

$N_1^0 = 30$

$N_2^0 = 20$

$N_3^0 = 20$

Figure 9

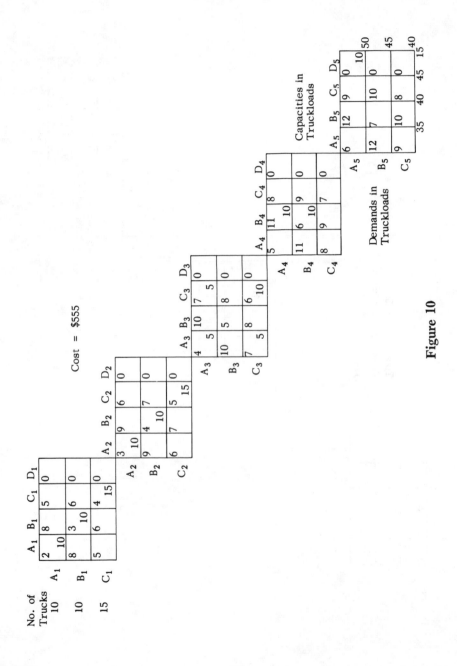

Figure 10

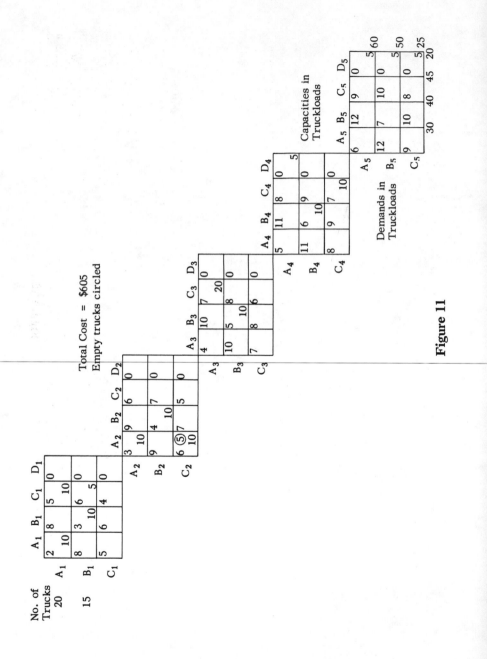

Figure 11

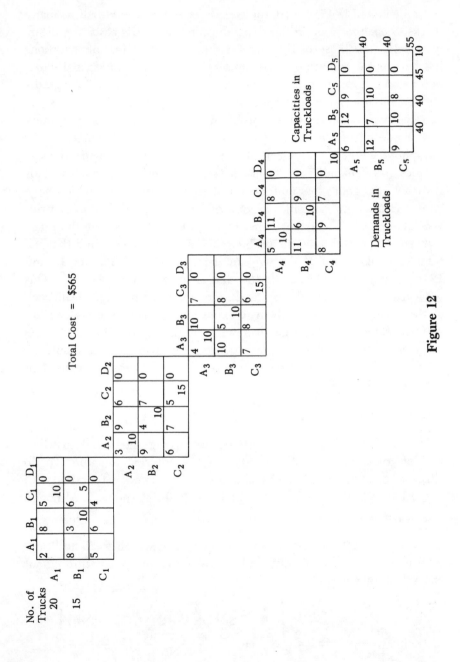

Figure 12

As illustrated in Figure 10, the scheduler sends exactly half as many trucks to each location in the same shipping plan. His costs are, clearly, exactly half those of the larger firm. The set of feasible solutions has been cut exactly to one half its original size. The functional equation passing through it, however, has not been changed and its gradient remains the same. The solution therefore rests on the exact same extreme point as in the larger problem. The extreme point was, however, made up of values one half the size of those in Figure 4.

Suppose we now take the problem of Figure 4 and divide the capacities and demands in half once more. This time, however, we shall distribute the goods less uniformly but still into two firms which have total demands and capacities exactly one half those of the larger firm. We let each of the smaller firms have half the trucks that the large firm employed and solve the problem again. This time we find that the total scheduling cost of the two small firms, $1,170, (Figures 11 and 12) is larger than that of the larger single firm, $1,080. This is clearly a case where the particular "hands of shipments" dealt each of the smaller firms leads them to have higher average costs per ton shipped than a single large firm with the same total tonnage. It is not clear, however, whether this difference in average cost should be attributed to economies of scale. In any case, our example is consistent with Warner's findings [22].

2.8 IMPUTED VALUES TO TRUCK CAPACITY

We shall next examine the effect of varying the initial distribution of trucks on the optimal value of the criterion function. To do this, we must find the rate of change of the criterion function with respect to N_i^o, the number of vehicles initially at source i. Although the distribution of trucks varies with each interval, this value $\dfrac{dC}{dN_i^o}$ gives the amount the system cost will change if we place an additional truck at source i initially, and leave it in the system throughout the scheduling period.

$$(66) \quad \frac{dC\,(N)}{dN_q^o} = \frac{\partial \left[\sum_{t=1}^{T} \sum_{i=1}^{I} \sum_{j=1}^{J} \sum_{p=0}^{P} {}_pC_{ij}^t \left({}_pN_{ij}^t \right) \right]}{\partial N_q^o}$$

$$-\sum_{i=1}^{I} w_i^1 \left(\frac{dN_i^o}{dN_q^o}\right) - \sum_{i=1}^{I} w_i^1 \; \partial \frac{\left[\sum\limits_{p=0}^{P} \sum\limits_{j=1}^{J} {}_pN_{ij}^1\right]}{\partial N_q^o}$$

$$-\sum_{t=1}^{T} \sum_{i=1}^{I} w_i^t \left(\frac{dN_i^o}{dN_q^o}\right) - \sum_{t=1}^{s} \sum_{i=1}^{I} w_i^t \; \partial \frac{\left[\sum\limits_{J=1}^{J} \sum\limits_{p=0}^{P} {}_pN_{ij}^t\right]}{\partial N_q^o}$$

$$+ \sum_{t=1}^{s-1} \sum_{i=1}^{I} w_i^t \; \partial \frac{\left[\sum\limits_{j=1}^{J} \sum\limits_{p=0}^{P} {}_pN_{ji}^t\right]}{\partial N_q^o}$$

$$s=2, \ldots, T$$

We can see directly that:

$$(67) \quad \partial \frac{\left[\sum\limits_{t=1}^{T} \sum\limits_{i=1}^{I} \sum\limits_{j=1}^{J} \sum\limits_{p=0}^{P} {}_pC_{ij}^t \; ({}_pN_{ij}^t)\right]}{\partial N_q^o} = 0$$

$$(68) \quad \partial \frac{\sum\limits_{p=0}^{P} \sum\limits_{j=1}^{J} {}_pN_{ij}^1}{\partial N_q^o} = 0,$$

$$(69) \quad \partial \frac{\sum\limits_{p=0}^{P} \sum\limits_{j=1}^{J} {}_pN_{ji}^t}{\partial N_q^o} = 0,$$

$$(70) \quad \frac{dN_i^o}{dN_q^o} = \begin{array}{l} 0 \; i \neq q \\ 1 \; i = q, \end{array}$$

or finally,

$$(71) \quad \frac{dC(N)}{dN_q^o} = \sum_{t=1}^{T} w_{|q}^t$$

Thus, $\frac{dC}{dN_q^o}$ is equal to the summation, over the period, of the imputed value of truck capacity at source p. In other words, the total change in system cost through the addition of a single truck at source p at the beginning of the period is given by expression (71).

Now, since w_i^t is the dual variable associated with the truck availability expressions of the primal problem, it will be zero if these
expressions are not met as equalities. This seems quite obvious, for
how can we change the total cost by adding more trucks to a source
if the trucks already there have not all been used? If, however, the
trucks at i are all used in interval t, then $w_i^t > 0$. By examining
these imputed values (the w_i^t) and summing them for each interval,
t, over the period, T, we can determine the magnitude of the cost
reduction possible through the addition of one truck at any source.
This will hold true, as the theory of parametric programming suggests,
only as long as the current solution basis is retained. Any addition of
trucks that results in a change of basis will necessitate a recomputa-
tion of the problem. It should be noted that the path through the
schedule, taken by the additional truck, has already been determined
by the optimal basis. The value of the additional truck will always
be found by summing the dual variables associated with the source

at which it enters the system. It is apparent that $\sum_{t=1}^{T} w_i^t$ also repre-

sents the amount the private or for-hire carrier should be willing to
pay for one extra truck at source i for one period.

Partial sums of w_i^t can be used to evaluate the value of truck capacity for any portion of the scheduling period. The value w_i^t as
previously mentioned represents the rent to truck capacity at source i
in interval t. It would be possible to calculate the cost of adding a truck
for only one interval if needed, say through a leasing arrangement, and
then to compare that to the reduction in system cost resulting from the
use of an additional truck over the interval in question. If we look at
the solution to the problem depicted in Figure 13, for example, and the
dual variables associated with source A in each interval (w_A^t) we find
that: $w_A^1 = 3$, $w_A^2 = 2$, $w_A^3 = 1$, $w_A^4 = 0$, and $w_A^5 = 0$.
A total of six units can be saved by adding an additional truck at
source A in the first interval and leaving it in the system for the
entire period. Figure 13 displays the allocation resulting from the
addition of the single truck at A. The cost has been reduced to \$1,104,
a savings of six dollars over all. We can save this amount for every

86

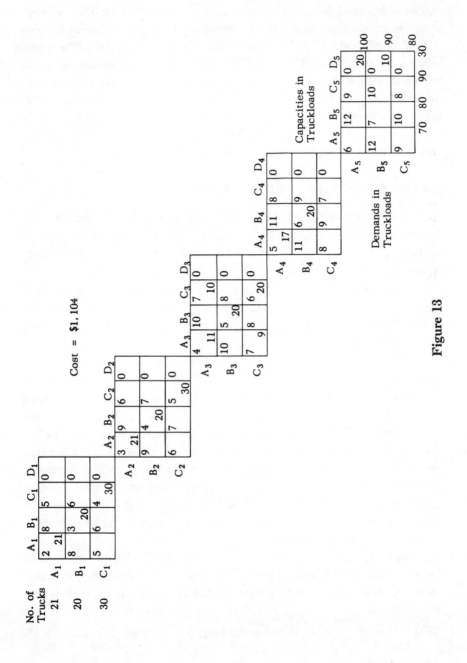

Figure 13

extra truck added at A until there is a change in basis. In other words, if the shipper could rent a truck at source A at the beginning of the first interval and use it for three intervals without consideration for where it was located at the end of third interval, he would do so if the truck rented for less than six dollars per *period*. Suppose, on the other hand, that trucks are rented for two dollars per *interval* at source A. Then the shipper will find that he is better off to rent a truck in the first interval. He will be indifferent in the second interval, and will not rent a truck in the third interval.

2.9 MULTI-PERIOD SCHEDULING

Earlier in this paper, the relationships inherent in scheduling over several periods were discussed but a multi-period model was not presented nor was the nature of the constraint matrix formed by this scheduling model discussed.

Suppose that the scheduler wishes to extend his planning horizon from one week to one month. He is still faced with weekly demands, but he knows these demands for one month in advance and wishes to know the schedule that his trucks should follow for the month. There are several reasons why the scheduler might want to perform this analysis.

First, it will tell him the allocation of his trucks in advance so that he can better schedule his drivers. Second, if he knows the route his trucks are to take for this longer period, (a month) he will be better able to consider maintenance problems. Third, scheduling for several periods in advance enables him to more efficiently use the computation facilities available to him. Fourth, scheduling over a month allows him to take into account the relationship between the minimum cost attainable for a period and the initial distribution of trucks for that period (i.e., the final distribution of the previous period).

Consider a scheduling period made up of K shorter subperiods (weeks) where the basic interval remains one day and $_p a_i^{T k}$ and $_p b_j^{T k}$ are respectively the capacities and demands in the kth week.

Then $\sum_{k=1}^{K} {}_p a_i^{T k}$ represents the total capacity at i used in the scheduling period and $\sum_{k=1}^{K} {}_pb_j^{Tk}$ the total scheduling period demand at j.

The problem may be formulated:

Minimize:

$$(72) \quad \sum_{t=1}^{T_K} \sum_{p=0}^{P} \sum_{i=1}^{I} \sum_{j=1}^{J} ({}_pC_{ij}^t) ({}_pN_{ij}^t)$$

subject to:

$$(73) \quad \sum_{t=T_h+1}^{T_k} \sum_{i=1}^{I} {}_pN_{ij}^t \geqq {}_pb_j^{Tk}$$

$$j=1, \ldots, J, k=1, \ldots, K, h=k\text{-}1, T_0=0, p=1, \ldots, P$$

$$(74) \quad \sum_{t=T_h+1}^{T_k} \sum_{j=1}^{J} {}_pN_{ij}^t \leqq {}_pa_i^{Tk}$$

$$i=1, \ldots, I, k=1, \ldots, K, h=k\text{-}1, T_0=0, p=1, \ldots, P$$

$$(75) \quad \sum_{j=1}^{J} \sum_{p=0}^{P} {}_pN_{ij}^1 \leqq N_i^o \qquad i=1, \ldots, I$$

$$(76) \quad \sum_{t=1}^{s} \sum_{j=1}^{J} \sum_{p=0}^{P} {}_pN_{ij}^t - \sum_{t=1}^{s-1} \sum_{j=1}^{J} \sum_{p=0}^{P} {}_pN_{ji}^t \leqq N_i^o$$

$$i=1, \ldots, I, s=2, \ldots, T_K$$

$$(77) \quad {}_pN_{ij}^t \leqq 0 \text{ all } i,j,p,t$$

Here each week is assumed to contain the same number of intervals, and the intervals (days) in the ith week are numbered from $T_{i-1}+1$ to T_i, the number in the next subperiod (week), $T_i + 1$ to T_{i+1} and so on, up to T_K, the last interval in the Kth or last subperiod.

The solution to the model depicted by expressions (72) through (77) gives the optimal scheduling pattern for K weeks, taking into account the fact that the distribution of trucks at the end of week k-1 will be the initial distribution of trucks in week k. This interrelationship between subperiods (weeks) is incorporated in the model through expression (76). This corresponds to the original node constraint but the index, t, now ranges from 1, the first interval, to T_K, the last. The form of the constraint matrix is shown in Figure 14. This is the classic multi-copy matrix of Charnes and Cooper [2] where the truck constraints form the coupling functions and the demand and capacity constraints form each copy. Thus, there will be K copies, one for each week or subperiod in the scheduling period (month). Several methods have been suggested for the solution of multi-copy type problems. All of these techniques depend upon the existence of large blocks of zeros in the constraint matrix. The method of Charnes and Cooper can serve as a representative example. The computational difficulties in our model stem from the size of the linear programming problem it generates. Since one of the contributing factors to the size of the problem is the number of intervals involved, the enormity of the problem can easily be demonstrated; it is K times the size of the one week model presented in expressions

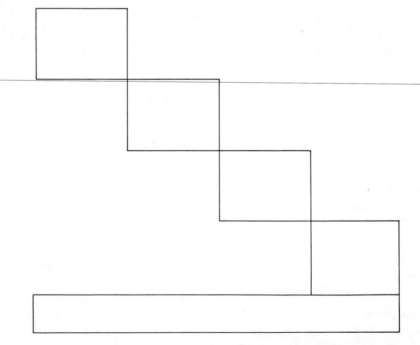

Figure 14

(16), (6), (8), (10), (11) and (17). Here K is taken as the number of weeks in the scheduling period. This size makes even special techniques quite cumbersome.

It is possible, however, to formulate an equivalent model that is more amenable to computation. The transformation of the original model results in a constraint matrix which is of the form called "intertwined" by Bellman. We can then employ an approach, suggested by Dantzig [3], to solve a series of smaller linear programming problems and thereby achieve a solution to our larger problem.

Instead of constraint [76], the following expressions are employed: In the first subperiod

$$(78) \quad \sum_{t=2}^{s} \sum_{j=1}^{J} \sum_{p=0}^{P} {}_pN_{ij}^t - \sum_{t=2}^{s-1} \sum_{j=1}^{J} \sum_{p=0}^{P} {}_pN_{ji}^t \leq N_i^o,$$

$$s=2, \ldots, T, \ i=1, \ldots, I, \text{ and}$$

$$(79) \quad \sum_{t=1}^{T_1} \sum_{j=1}^{J} \sum_{p=0}^{P} {}_pN_{ji}^t - \sum_{t=1}^{T_1} \sum_{j=1}^{J} \sum_{p=0}^{P} {}_pN_{ij}^t + N_i^o + a_i^{T_1}, = 0,$$

$$i=1, \ldots, I.$$

Thereafter,

$$(80) \quad \sum_{t=T_h+1}^{s} \sum_{j=1}^{J} \sum_{p=0}^{P} {}_pN_{ij}^t - \sum_{t=T_h+1}^{s-1} \sum_{j=1}^{J} \sum_{p=0}^{P} {}_pN_{ji}^t - a_i^{T_h} \leq 0,$$

$$S=1+T_h, \ldots, T_k, \ k=2, \ldots, K, \ h=k-1$$

$$i=1, \ldots, I, \text{ and}$$

$$(81) \quad \sum_{t=T_h+1}^{s} \sum_{j=1}^{J} \sum_{p=0}^{P} {}_pN_{ji}^t - \sum_{t=T_h+1}^{s-1} \sum_{j=1}^{J} \sum_{p=0}^{P} {}_pN_{ij}^t - a_i^{T_k} + a_i^{T_h} = 0,$$

$$k=2, \ldots K, \ h=k-1, \ i=1, \ldots, I.$$

$a_i^{T_h}$ represents the number of trucks available at source i in the kth period. It is found by subtracting the number of trucks leaving i during the subperiod from those entering. The variable $a_k^{T_h}$ is the final distribution of trucks in the hth period (h=k-1). If these constraints are substituted for expression (76), the constraint matrix takes on the form shown in Figure 15.

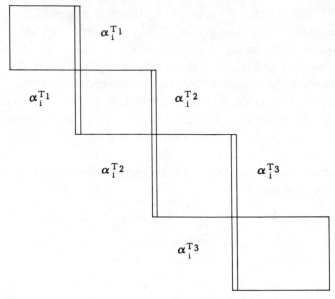

Figure 15

Thus, the variables $\alpha_j^{T_h}$ and $\alpha_i^{T_k}$ are common to stages h and k (h=k-1) and we have the equivalent formulation of the "intertwined" type of Bellman. This formulation will yield the same solution as the multi-copy form. It is possible, however, to solve this system using the dynamic programming technique developed by Bellman. This technique involves the solution of several of the smaller problems presented earlier.

Consider the Kth subperiod (i.e., the last week in the month). The only variable appearing in this and in a different subperiod is $\alpha_i^{T_{K-1}}$, the number of trucks at source i at the start of subperiod K. Suppose the Kth subperiod scheduling problem is solved for every possible set of initial truck distributions, $(\alpha_1^{T_{K-1}}, \ldots, \alpha_I^{T_{K-1}})_m = A_m^{K-1}$, the m-th set of initial distributions, where $\sum_{i=1}^{I} \alpha_i^{T_{K-1}} = X$ the total number of trucks available. That is, the trucks are divided among the I sources in every possible way, and for each division the scheduling problem is solved. The number of possible initial distributions is finite

and equal to $\dfrac{(X+I-1)!}{(I-1)!X!}$. This procedure assumes no specifications

on the final distribution of vehicles at the end of the Kth subperiod. There is a value of the Kth subperiod objective function, $_mf_K$ (A_m^{K-1}) associated with each initial distribution vector, A_m^{K-1} and the single period (the Kth) cost minimizing problem.

Now consider the next to last subperiod, period K-1. Again consider all of the possible initial distribution of vehicles, A_m^{K-2}. Each initial distribution, A_m^{K-2}, will generate many feasible (though not necessarily cost minimizing) final distributions. Many of these final distributions will be among the set of vectors, A_m^{K-1} generated above. Some of the possible initial distributions, A_m^{K-2} may not generate any final distributions among the A_m^{K-1} set. These initial distributions are therefore infeasible from the point of view of the over-all problem and are henceforth ignored. Each combination of A_i^{K-2} and A_j^{K-1} is associated with a cost for the (K-1)-st period scheduling problem, $R(A_i^{K-2}, A_j^{K-1})$. As before, each vector A_j^{K-1} is associated with a cost for the Kth period $_jf_K$ (A_j^{K-1}). Now evaluate:

$$(82) \quad _mf_{K-1}(A_m^{K-2}) \quad = \min_{A_m^{K-1}} \left\{ R(A_m^{K-2}, \ A_m^{K-1}) \ + \ _mf_K(A_m^{K-1}) \right\}$$

In other words, for each A_m^{K-1} take the minimum value of $R(A_m^{K-2}, A_m^{K-1})$ and add the cost $_mf_K(A_m^{K-1})$. This process gives an implicit relationship between A_m^{K-2} and $_mf_{K-1}(A_m^{K-1})$. Now, for each value of A_m^{K-2}, the minimizing procedure has specified a value of A_m^{K-1}. For the rest of the periods (e.g., K-2, K-3 etc.) we need only consider A_m^{K-2} and never go back to A_m^{K-1}. For example, consider subperiod K-2. A_m^{K-2} is the final distribution of trucks for this subperiod. The analysis for subperiod ("week") K-1 is now repeated for all A_m^{K-2} and A_m^{K-3} instead of A_m^{K-2} and A_m^{K-1}. For each A_m^{K-2} evaluate $R(A_m^{K-3}, A_m^{K-2})$ with every possible vector A_m^{K-3}. Now

$$(83) \quad _mf_{K-2}(A_m^{K-3}) \ = \min_{A_m^{K-2}} \left\{ R(A_m^{K-3}, \ A_m^{K-2}) \ + \ _mf_{K-1}(A_m^{K-2}) \right\}$$

thus for each possible A_m^{K-3} the optimal schedule from subperiod K-2 on is obtained.

This procedure is continued until the first subperiod is reached. Here the N_{im}^{o}'s are found as the initial distribution. Thus for each $A_m^1 = (a_1^{T_1}, \ldots, a_1^{T_1})$, the $R(N_i^{o}, A_m^1)$ is evaluated and N_i^{o} is found from:

$$(84) \quad {}^*f_1(N_i^{o}) = \min_{A_m^1} \left\{ R(N_i^{o}, A_m^1) + {}_mf_2(A_m^1) \right\}$$

where $^*f_1(N_i^{o})$ is the optimal solution to the K subperiod scheduling problem.

This method is at least as cumbersome as it seems. When X is large or there are a great many sources, the number of computations is enormous. The use of parametric programming in the evaluation of $R(A_m^{k-1}, A_m^k)$ may be of some help, but in general a big problem remains and the solution is not easily found.

2.10 DECENTRALIZED DECISIONS: AN ALTERNATIVE MEANS OF COMPUTATION

Return now to the problem as depicted in Figure 14. This problem can be treated as $K+1$ linear programming problems where K of the problems are of the form:

$$(85) \quad \min \sum_{t=T_h+1}^{T_k} \sum_{i=1}^{I} \sum_{j=1}^{J} \sum_{p=0}^{P} {}_pC_{ij}^t \, ({}_pN_{ij}^t) + \sum_{i=1}^{I} d_i^{T_h} \left(a_i^{T_h} \right)$$

$$(86) \quad \text{st.} \sum_{t=T_h+1}^{T_k} \sum_{i=1}^{I} {}_pN_{ij}^t \geqq {}_pb_j^{T_k} \qquad j=1, \ldots, J, \; h=k-1,$$
$$p=1, \ldots, P,$$

$$(87) \quad \sum_{t=T_h+1}^{T_k} \sum_{j=1}^{J} {}_pN_{ij}^t \leqq {}_pa_i^{T_k} \qquad i=1, \ldots, I, \; h=k-1,$$
$$p=1, \ldots, P$$

$$(88) \quad \sum_{j=1}^{J} \sum_{p=0}^{P} {}_pN_{ij}^{T_h+1} - a_i^{T_h} \geqq 0 \qquad i=1, \ldots, I$$

$$(89) \quad \sum_{t=T_h+1}^{s} \sum_{j=1}^{J} \sum_{p=0}^{P} {}_pN_{ij}^t - \sum_{t=T_h+1}^{s-1} \sum_{j=1}^{J} \sum_{p=0}^{P} {}_pN_{ji}^t - a_i^{T_h} \geqq 0$$
$$i=1, \ldots, I, \; s=T_h+2, \ldots, T_K$$

The other LP problem, representing the coupling relation, is:

$$(90) \quad \min \sum_{t=1}^{T_K} \sum_{i=1}^{I} \sum_{j=1}^{J} \sum_{p=0}^{P} {}_pC_{ij}^t \left({}_pN_{ij}^t\right) + \sum_{t=1}^{K} \sum_{i=1}^{I} d_i^{T_h} \left(a_i^{T_h}\right)$$

$$(91) \quad \text{st.} \quad - \sum_{t=T_h+1}^{T_k} \sum_{j=1}^{J} \sum_{p=0}^{P} {}_pN_{ij}^t + \sum_{t=T_h+1}^{T_k} \sum_{j=1}^{J} \sum_{p=0}^{P} {}_pN_{ji}^t$$

$$+ \ a_i^{T_h} - a_i^{T_k} = 0 \qquad i=1, \ldots, I, \ k=1, \ldots, K$$
$$h=k\text{-}1, \ T_0=0$$

(92) and $a_i^{T_0} = N_i^o$ in the previous notation.

This formulation suggests a decentralized firm where one of the divisions is marketing and the other shipping. The marketing department takes a forecasted demand for each good at each sink for, say the kth subperiod (i.e., kth "week" of the "month"), and solves that one of the preceding K, LP problems referring to the kth subperiod. It uses production data to determine the supplies (i.e., the ${}_pa_i^{T_k}$) and its forecasts to determine the demands (i.e., the ${}_pb_j^{T_k}$). The line-haul costs are provided by the shipping department and in this initial solution they set $d_i^{T_h} = 0$, $(i=1, \ldots, I)$ that is, it costs the kth subperiod marketing department[2] nothing to select the optimal initial distribution of trucks for the kth subperiod. The marketing departments send their optimal solutions to the shipping department for evaluation. The shipping department's LP problem is given by expressions 90-92. Its problem concerns the way in which the initial truck distribution of one subperiod influences the costs of the following subperiod. Upon receiving the optimal basic feasible solutions of the marketing department's problems (expressions 85-89), the shipping department will test their feasibility in its own LP problem. The shipping department then makes changes in the cost coefficients of each marketing department's problem, based on the imputed

---

[2]It is sometimes convenient to treat the marketing department as if it were itself broken into sections with each section assigned to one subperiod of the month. In a sense, these marketing subsections compete with each other through the initial truck distribution relationship. The value of the trucks to each subsection is reflected in the values of the $d_i^{T_h}$ assigned by the department which is using this "pricing" device to allocate its supply of trucks in order to minimize transport costs over the whole period.

vehicle values for the whole system. This leads to a redistribution of trucks tending toward an over-all optimum as described by expression 90. The marketing department will then solve its problem again and send these solutions back to the shipping department for additional cost adjustments.

This is the classic decomposition technique of Dantzig and Wolfe [6] which has been shown to reach an optimal solution to the over-all problem in a finite and usually small number of iterations. The association of decomposition with the decentralized firm has recently been described by Baumol and Fabian [1]. It is easy to see the computational power in this method. A problem with $K[IP+JP] + IT_K$ constraints has been transformed into K problems with $IP + JP + IT$ (T intervals in a subperiod) constraints and one problem with IK constraints. Since the limiting factor in most LP computer codes is not the number of variables, but the number of constraints, it is possible to solve much larger problems using the decomposition method than by a direct solution of expressions 72-77.

In detail the method is as follows. Let $^1N^k$ be the vector which represents the first solution to the kth subperiod scheduling problem. This will be sent from the marketing department to the shipping department. $^1N^k$ contains the optimal values of the $_pN_{ij}^t$'s, a_i^{Th} and slack variables. The shipping department then takes $^1N^k$ which is a vector of real numbers and creates the weighted sums $^1\lambda^k \; _pN_{ij}^t = {}^*{}_pN_{ij}^t$, and $(^1\lambda^k) a_i^{Th} = {}^*a_i^{Th}$. The weights $^1\lambda^k \leq 1$, are now the unknowns to be found in the problem:

$$(93) \quad \min \sum_{t=1}^{T_K} \sum_{i=1}^{I} \sum_{j=1}^{J} \sum_{p=0}^{P} {}_pC_{ij}^t \, (^*{}_pN_{ij}^t) + \sum_{k=1}^{K} \sum_{i=1}^{I} d_i^{Th} \, (^*a_i^{Th})$$

$$(94) \quad \text{st.} \; -\sum_{t=T_h+1}^{T_k} \sum_{j=1}^{J} \sum_{p=0}^{P} {}^*{}_pN_{ij}^t + \sum_{t=T_h+1}^{T_k} \sum_{j=1}^{J} \sum_{p=0}^{P} {}^*{}_pN_{ij}^t$$

$$+ \, {}^*a_i^{Th} - {}^*a_i^{Tk} = 0 \qquad i=1, \ldots, T, \; k=1, \ldots, k$$
$$h=k\text{-}1, \; T_0=0$$

$$(95) \quad {}^1\lambda^k \leq 1 \qquad k=1, \ldots, K$$

In other words, first solve for the cost minimizing factors $^1\lambda^k$ which premultiply the known vectors $^1N^k$. Then look at the vector of dual variables $\pi = (\pi_{11}, \ldots, \pi_{IK}, \bar{\pi}_1, \ldots, \bar{\pi}_K)$, where π_{ik} is the dual variable associated with the slack variable for the ith source in the kth subperiod and $\bar{\pi}_i$ is the dual variable associated with the constraint $^1\lambda^k \leq 1$. In a sense, π_{ik} represents the marginal value, to the over-all schedule, of the trucks at source i in subperiod k.

The shipping department then calculates the new unit costs, $_p^1 C_{ij}^t$ where $_p^1 C_{ij}^t = {}_p C_{ij}^t - ({}_p a_{ij}^t \pi_{ik})$ where $_p a_{ij}^t$ represents the co-efficient (either ± 1 or 0) of $^*_p N_{ij}^t$ in the constraints of the shipping department's LP problem. It also calculates $^1 d_i^{T_h} = d_i^{T_h} - (a_i^{T_h} \pi_{ih})$ where $a_i^{T_h} = \pm 1$, depending on the subperiod. The appropriate π_{ik} must be picked to correspond to each $_p C_{ij}^t$ or $d_i^{T_h}$. If $1 \leq t \leq T_1$, pick π_{i1}, if $T_1+1, \leq t \leq T_2$ pick π_{i2} etc.

These new values $_p^1 C_{ij}^t$ and $^1 d_i^{T_h}$ are sent back to the marketing department and they solve the same LP problem (85-89) as before but with the new costs $_p^1 C_{ij}^t$ and $^1 d_i^{T_h}$. Call these new optimal solutions $^2 N^k$, the second solution to the kth subperiod's scheduling problem.

The shipping department then takes these second solution vectors and calculates $^*_p N_{ij}^t = {}^1\lambda^k \, {}^1 N^k + {}^2\lambda^k \, {}^2 N^k$, $^*a_i^{T_h} = {}^1\lambda^k \, {}^1 N^k + {}^2\lambda^k \, {}^2 N^k$, using the appropriate $_p N_{ij}^t$ and $a_i^{T_h}$'s of $^1 N^k$, and $^2 N^k$, so that each new variable can be represented as some constant times $^1\lambda^k$ (which is again to be determined) and $^2\lambda^k$ a new variable. It then solves the problem.

$$(93) \quad \min \sum_{t=1}^{T_K} \sum_{i=1}^{I} \sum_{j=1}^{J} \sum_{p=0}^{P} {}_p C_{ij}^t \, (^*_p N_{ij}^t) + \sum_{k=1}^{K} \sum_{i=1}^{I} d_i^{T_h} \, (^*a_i^{T_h})$$

$$(94) \quad \text{st.} \quad -\sum_{t=T_h+1}^{T_K} \sum_{j=1}^{J} \sum_{p=0}^{P} {}^*_p N_{ij}^t + \sum_{t=T_h+1}^{T_h} \sum_{j=1}^{J} \sum_{p=0}^{P} {}^*_p N_{ij}^t$$

$$+ {}^*a_i^{T_h} - {}^*a_i^{T_k} = 0 \quad i=1, \ldots, I, \, k=1, \ldots, K$$

$$h=k\text{-}1, \quad T_0=0.$$

$$(96) \quad \sum_{i=1}^{2} {}^1\lambda^k = 1 \quad k=1, \ldots, K$$

This problem is solved for the optimal values of $^1\lambda^k$, the coefficients of $^1N^k$, to determine a basic feasible solution to the over-all problem.[3]

Next, the shipping department again forms the vector of dual variables $\pi = (\pi_{11}, \ldots, \pi_{Ik}; \bar{\pi}_1, \ldots, \bar{\pi}_k)$. Using the values of $^1\lambda^k$ which were just obtained, it solves for the cost of the kth subperiod's schedule, i.e., $^1\lambda^k {}^1N^k + {}^2\lambda^k {}^2N^k$ as the vector of shipments and initial distributions. Call this cost C^k, the cost of shipping in subperiod k. If $-C^k > \pi_k$, then new $_pC_{ij}^t$'s must be calculated for that subperiod.[4] If $-C^k \leqq \bar{\pi}_k$, they are left as $^1_pC_{ij}^t$, and $^1d_i^{Th}$. Now, if $-C^k > \bar{\pi}_k$ holds for any k, this means that the problem must be solved again for every subperiod by the marketing department with new costs calculated from the new π_{ik}'s. These new costs will be called $^2_pC_{ij}^t$ and $^2d_i^{Th}$ and will be found in the same way that $^1_pC_{ij}^t$ and $^1d_i^{Th}$ were found. This technique is continued until $- C^k \leqq \bar{\pi}_k$, for all k=1, . . . , K. At that point the $^1\lambda^{k}$'s, which are in the optimal solution to the shipping department's problem, are used to weight each of the $^1N^k$'s and the total or over-all optimal solution for the kth subperiod problem is the vectors:

$$(97) \quad {}^*N^k = \sum_i {}^i\lambda^k {}^iN^k, \ k=1, \ldots, K.$$

When comparing $-C^k$ with $\bar{\pi}_k$, one is testing whether the new divisional subperiod solution improves the over-all solution. Here $\bar{\pi}_k$ represents the over-all value of the new solutions to subperiod k. When this gain is no longer greater than the subperiods cost the optimal solution has been obtained. In other words, the decomposition principle is used to determine the appropriate costs for each movement scheduled by the marketing department. These costs are the final (optimal) values of $^q_pC_{ij}^t$ and $^qd_i^{Th}$ if q different solutions are re-

---

[3] Notice that the weights given to past marketing department solutions, the $^i\lambda^k$, are all determined anew at each iteration.

[4] $-\bar{\pi}_k$ is the *total* cost contributed to the over-all program by subperiod k under the terms currently proposed by the shipping department's program. C^k is the vector of revised cost figures for the Kth subperiod being given by $^1_pC_{ij} = {}_pC_{ij}^t - {}_pa_{ij}^t \pi_{ik}$ and $^1d_i^{Th} = d_i^{Th} - a_i^{Th} \pi_{ih}$. If $-C^k > \bar{\pi}_k$ or $\bar{\pi}_k + C^k < 0$ then $\bar{\pi}_k < 0$ and $(-\bar{\pi}_k) > 0$ so $(-\bar{\pi}_k) > C^k$ and the over-all costs of the shipping department problem can be lowered by taking the most recently calculated marketing department program, $^2N^k$, and averaging it with programs previously proposed.

quired before an optimum is reached. These costs take account of not only the direct shipping costs but also the effect of a shipment in one period on the level of attainable costs in the next period. In other words, they represent the true cost to the system of making any particular shipment when the other shipments all are made optimally. If the optimal values of each ${}_p^q C_{ij}^t$ and ${}^q d_i^{Th}$ were known in advance, by some mysterious means, the optimal multi-period scheduling problem could be solved as a set of *independent* single period problems and still the over-all optimal would be attained.

There are any number of ways in which the larger problem could have been broken down into a number of smaller ones. Subperiods could have been grouped, for instance, into two or three "weeks" at a time. Perhaps the most interesting variation is the following one. Consider the same K marketing department problems as before (one for each week). For the shipping department's constraint, however, require only that, say, for subperiod k, $a^h = a^{k-1}$. That is, the initial distribution of trucks in subperiod k was the final distribuiton of subperiod k-1. This is essentially what was done in the model developed here. However, suppose this restriction could be written solely in terms of the a_i^{Th}'s. Then the only prices that would be changed at each iteration would be the d_i^{Th}'s or prices of the initial distribution of each subperiod. This would clearly define a competitive situation between the subperiods for distributions of trucks with which to start the subperiod. (See footnote 2 p. 95.)

This latter formulation lends itself to many other interesting applications. For example, consider the allocation of a mobile factor of production among geographically distinct regions of an economy, the allocation to be made in order to achieve some economy wide goal while the regions retain autonomy in the pursuit of their own objectives. The conflict between objectives is resolved, in order to achieve the over-all goal, through a regionally discriminating pricing mechanism for the mobile factor input. Further applications will be explored in subsequent papers.

2.11 CONCLUDING REMARKS

Certain conditions were ignored in the foregoing models. The operator was assumed to have the same number of trucks throughout the problem. Thus, a breakdown of one or more trucks was not considered. The cost of congestion, i.e., the fact that the number of trucks going between two nodes might influence the transportation costs, was ignored. The assumption of linearity was discussed in the first part of the paper. The question of whether the real world can or cannot be treated as linear is clearly an empirical one. As mentioned earlier linear programming gives us so much information about the system we feel justified in making the linearity assumption, at least as a first approximation.

Possible extensions of the models presented are numerous. Considerations of probability distributions determining future demands or costs lead to stochastic programming problems. A problem which might be faced by a firm just entering into the trucking business is: What size fleet would be best from the standpoint of efficiency and capital limitations? The buy or lease question might be considered or any number of the investment problems concerning the operation of truck fleets. It is certainly true that a good deal more would be involved in the analysis of problems of this nature than the scheduling aspect. It would help the investor, however, if he knew approximately what his fleet requirements would be and the costs which would be associated with scheduling alone. Firms considering the use of private carriage and common carrier operators might find it extremely helpful.

The authors do not know what method firms now in operation use to schedule their fleets. Some of them, especially the smaller firms in terms of fleet size, more than likely trust all scheduling to an experienced dispatcher. The method shown requires the use of digital computers and special programs. It is possible that for large problems a large amount of computer time is essential for a solution. The small problems shown as examples in the paper required up to six minutes to solve, but these solutions included shadow costs and parametric programming on requirements and costs. The smaller operation might find the cost of obtaining a solution as big a cost as the loss which they might incur by scheduling in some other manner and not achieving an "optimal" solution. It is quite possible that only part of the schedule might be programmed and the other part done by traditional methods.

Another area which might be of some interest in furthering the work of this paper is in the determination of the optimal length of the scheduling period. We have assumed, for convenience, that the operator scheduled his trucks to handle weekly system demands. If he knew his demands for a longer length of time the scheduling period might be lengthened. Two cases of this nature might be investigated. In the first, the demands might be satisfied over the scheduling period, say one month, in any manner. This is analogous to the weekly demands set forth in this paper. The second case attempts to take a more realistic view to the monthly demands. A certain portion of the demand must be satisfied in each week, while the balance can be satisfied at any time over the month. The third case in which weekly demands made up the entire month's demands has been solved. In this way the difference between an "optimal" schedule over time and a "constrained optimal" could be determined. In any case, it would be interesting to investigate the relationship between the length of the period and the cost of scheduling. If the period were lengthened it would be possible to have shipments on days that would ordinarily have been prohibited. An example of this would be the shipment of goods between nodes that are two or more intervals apart on what would have ordinarily been the last day of the original period, but is now just another day in the longer period. The additional length of the period might also be an opportunity for some of the trucks to leave the system for servicing during the period itself.

The models presented in this paper have attempted to capture the generally important elements of the scheduling problems faced by truck operators—private or for-hire. The list of extensions, by no means complete, indicates that the problem has not been satisfactorily solved. Although considerable work has been done, much more remains before the fleet operator has an adequate planning tool for both his scheduling and his longer range fleet planning problems.

Appendix

The cost function used in the models presented in this paper is of the basic form

$$(A1) \qquad C_{ij} = C'_{ij} + \gamma_i + \lambda_j,$$

where C'_{ij} is the line-haul cost; γ_i is the terminal cost at source i; and λ_j is the terminal cost of unloading a truck at sink j.

Line-haul costs have been shown to rise linearly with distance. The relationship is represented graphically in Figure A1 [14].

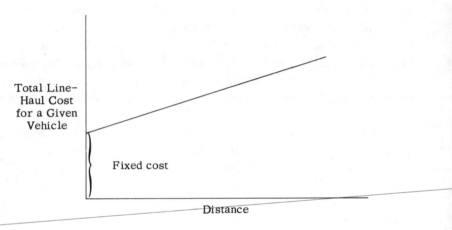

Figure A1

For any node to node movement there is a specific distance d_{ij} and by multiplying this distance times the rate represented above, we get the out-of-pocket cost of sending a truck from i to j, say C'_{ij}.

The fixed element shown in figure A1 represents maintenance, insurance, and license costs which must be paid whether or not the vehicle is used. For the shipper, the per period cost of these fixed items for his whole fleet will depend on the number of vehicles he owns and the length of the scheduling period. Both of these are treated as fixed parameters in the scheduling problem. For convenience, let us label the total of fixed line-haul costs, T.

The terminal cost of any particular node is a function of the shipment weight and the number of shipments. This relationship for a given shipment weight is represented graphically in Figure A2.

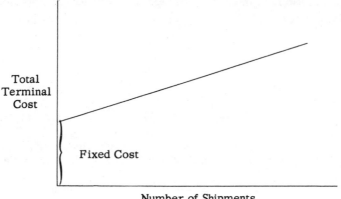

Figure A2

Terminal costs may differ from node to node due to geographical differences in the input prices. Note that differences in shipment weights among products have been ignored.

If we knew the number of shipments going into or leaving a node in any period it would be possible to obtain the terminal cost per shipment by looking at the slope of the appropriate curve at that point. If we call the terminal costs per shipment of loading trucks at source i, γ_i, and the costs per shipment of unloading goods at sink j, λ_j, we have a clear picture of the formulation of our cost function.

Our total cost function may be written,

$$(A2) \quad C = \sum_{t=1}^{T} \sum_{p=0}^{P} \sum_{i=1}^{I} \sum_{j=1}^{J} [(C'_{ij} + \gamma_i + \lambda_i) (_pN^t_{ij})] + R + T,$$

where R is the total fixed cost of the terminal operations. R is a constant in this problem because the number of nodes is fixed.

The formulation of the private carrier scheduling problem, presented in the text, uses the minimization of the shipping costs, C'_{ij}, and unloading costs, λ_j, as the objective. The loading costs were included in the U_i dual variables. Since the number of shipments *arriving* at any demanding site is known from the constraints of the prob-

103

lem while the number of shipments leaving any supply area is not, this unsymmetric treatment of loading and unloading costs seemed appropriate.

REFERENCES

[1] Baumol, W. J. and Fabian, T. "Decomposition, Pricing for Decentralization and External Economies," *Management Science* Vol. 11, No. 1, Sept. 1964.

[2] Charnes, A. and Cooper W. W. *Management Models and Industrial Applications of Linear Programming.* Vol. II. New York: John Wiley and Sons, Inc. 1961.

[3] Dantzig, G. B. "On the Status of Multistage Linear Programming Problems," *Management Science*, 6, 53-72, (1959).

[4] Dantzig, G. B. and Ferguson, A. R., "The Allocation of Aircraft to Routes—An Example of Linear Programming Under Uncertain Demand," *Management Science*, 10, 45-55 (1956).

[5] Dantzig, B. B. and Ramser, J. H. "The Truck Dispatching Problem," *Management Science*, 6, 80-91 (1959).

[6] Dantzig, G. B., and Wolfe, P., "Decomposition Principle for Linear Programs," *Operations Research*, Vol. 8, No. 1, Jan.-Feb., 1960.

[7] Dorfman, Robert, Samuelson, P. A., and Solow, R. M. *Linear Programming and Economic Analysis.* New York: McGraw-Hill Book Company, Inc. 1958, p. 454.

[8] Flood, M. M. "Application of Transportation Theory to Scheduling a Military Tanker Fleet," *Operations Research*, 2, 150-162 (1954).

[9] Ford, L. R. and Fulkerson, D. R. *Flows in Networks.* Princeton: The Princeton Press, 1962.

[10] Hadley, G. *Linear Programming.* Reading, Mass.: Addison-Wesley. 1962.

[11] Haley, K. B. "The Solid Transportation Problem," *Operations Research*, Vol. 10, 448-463 (1962).

[12] Henderson, James N. and Quandt, Richard E. *Microeconomic Theory.* New York: McGraw-Hill Book Company, Inc. 1958.

[13] Interstate Commerce Commission, *Cost of Transporting Freight by Class I and Class II Motor Carriers of General Commodities Midwest Territory,* 1960, Statement No. 2-60.

[14] Koopmans, T. C. (ed.). *Activity Analysis of Production and Allocation.* New York: John Wiley and Sons, Inc., 1951.

[15] Miller, Robert F. "An Analysis of a Motor Freight Scheduling Problem," Engineering Experiment Station, College of Engineering, The Ohio State University Press, Columbus, Vol. 31, No 1 (Jan. 1962).

[16] Miller, Ronald E. *"Domestic Airline Efficiency, an Application of Linear Programming."* Cambridge: The MIT Press (1962).

[17] Mills, Harlan D. "Marginal Values of Matrix Games and Linear Programs," *Linear Inequalities and Related Systems.* H. W. Kuhn and A. V. Tucker (eds), No. 38 in Annals of Mathematics Studies of Princeton University. Princeton: Princeton University Press, 1956, p. 183-193.

[18] Oi, Walter Y., Hurter, Arthur P. Jr. *The Economics of Private Truck Transportation.* Dubuque: Wm. C. Brown Company Publishers. (1965).

[19] Orden, Alex. "The Transshipment Problem," *Management Science,* II, 258-276, (April, 1956).

[20] Samuelson, Paul, "Frank Knight's Theorem in Linear Programming," *Zietschrift fur Nationalokonomie,* 18: August 1958, pp. 310-317.

[21] Uzawa, Hirofumi, "A Note on the Menger-Wieser Theory of Imputation," *Zietschrift fur Nationalokonomie,* 18: August 1958, pp. 318-334.

[22] Warner, Stanley. "Cost Models, Measurement Errors, and Economies of Scale in Trucking," *The Cost of Trucking: Econometric Analysis.* Dubuque: Wm. C. Brown Company Publishers. (1965).

Chapter 3

Economics of Private Carriage: A Case Study*

3.1 INTRODUCTION

Our point of departure is straightforward. It is unlikely that a regulated transportation tariff structure will be consistent with efficient pricing of transport resources. Private carriers can, if they wish, use efficient shadow prices, and in any case, there usually will exist tariff sets that can be employed more profitably than a given inefficient set.

Our *modus operandi* is extremely simple. We have collected considerable data from a wholesale grocer operating private motor carriage on intercity hauls throughout the United States. These data permit estimation (sometimes of a rough-and-ready type) of:

1. "production functions" specifying direct input requirements for hauls of various goods between any two points;
2. direct costs of such hauls, upon costing the inputs required in (1);
3. comparison of these direct costs with posted common-carrier tariffs;
4. imputation of nondirect costs to the activities, employing alternative rules;

*M. L. Burstein[1] and J. Egan[2] assisted by E. Glustoff.[3]

[1]Professor Burstein's paper was prepared while he was with Northwestern University and associated with the Transportation Center. He is now Visiting Professor of Economics at the University of Birmingham.

[2]University of Chicago, Department of Economics.

[3]Stanford University, Department of Economics.

5. estimation of the annual profitabilities of various private carriage activities, taking account of capital tied up in the ventures;
6. consideration of the over-all profitability of the company's operation.

We make these estimates. Emphasizing, as we do, the narrowly inductive foundations of our paper, we hesitate to generalize. Still, if forced (at the drop of a hat) to make broader inferences, we should make these points:

1. Motor haulage does not appear to entail large enough sunk costs to imply that tariffs would fall precipitously from "normal" competitive levels during periods of excess capacity;[4] economies of scale are not important;
2. regulated freight-rate structures appear badly to reflect cost differentials and, accordingly, to prevent common-carriage from attaining long-run efficiency pricing;
3. regulated freight-rate structures prevent tariffs from effectively reflecting excess capacities or varying degrees of scarcity in the short-run;
4. the extraordinary mobility of road-haulage equipment, together with other basic conditions of the industry, suggest that, subject to several *caveats*, the industry is uniquely suited to unregulated competition;
5. regulated tariffs on longer hauls appear to be particularly inefficient;
6. a meaningful amount of private-carriage activity might be prompted by considerations cited here;
7. optimal employment of private carriage requires frequent, wellnigh continuous, adjustment of shadow prices and shifting of equipment in response to shadow-price changes; indeed it is unlikely that a competitive market structure could attain such flexibility;
8. facet (7) might have important bearing on the theory of vertical integration.

---

[4]Thus it would not appear that arguments, stressing that equilibrium expected profit can be lower if variance of profit is reduced, are applicable here; the expected variance of profitability of transport operation under competition would not be exceptionally large.

3.2 PRICE THEORY

Some general notions are important both for analysis of specific private carriage activities and for making inferences from such analysis. A simple stock-flow model reveals much. Consider a system in which standard outfits of equipment are rented out by "source holders" who make a market for old sources and acquire new sources from manufacturers. Old and new sources are measured in standard efficiency units.[5] Carriers rent equipment from source holders and provide shipping services for firms and households. We consider only returns earned by carriers over direct carriage expense.

We begin by constraining the variables so as to determine market clearance at time t. If market clearance can be assured at all times, the following equation system can be applied recursively to generate a sequence of outcomes.

(1) $$s_t = \Phi(p_t)$$

(2) $$d_t = I_t + kS_t$$

(3) $$I_t = \lambda(D_t - S_t)$$

(4) $$D_t = \Psi(p_t, r_t, i_t^\varrho)$$

(5) $$S_t = S_o + \int_{-\infty}^{t} I_d\theta$$

(6) $$s = d_t$$

(7) $$r_t = f(S_t, \beta)$$

The system is comprised, then, of seven equations in the seven unknowns s_t, d_t, I_t D_t, S_t, p_t, and r_t. If non-negativity and other boundary conditions are met, it can be solved for the unknowns at t and, to repeat, a recursive process can be generated if there is continuous market clearance.

Equation 1 defines the flow rate of supply of sources (s_t) as a function of the price of sources (p_t). Equation 2 defines the flow

---

[5]*Cf.* M. L. Burstein, "The Demand for Household Refrigeration in the United States," in A. C. Harberger (ed), The Demand for Durable Goods (Chicago: University of Chicago Press; 1960), pp. 99-145. Also M. L. Burstein, "The Measurement of Quality Changes in Consumer Durables," *Manchester, School,* Vol. 29, No. 3 (September, 1961).

rate of demand for sources (d_t) as the sum of investment demand (I_t) and replacement demand (kS_t), where k is a depreciation rate and S_t is the stock of sources at t. Equation 3 defines the flow rate of investment demand as a number obtained by scaling D_t-S_t by λ, where D_t is the desired stock at t, which sometimes is called the potential stock. λ converts a number with the dimension of a stock into one with the dimension of a flow. Equation 4 defines D_t as a function of p_t, the rent of sources (r_t), and an exogenous discount rate (i_t^o). Equation 5 defines S_t historically. Equation 6 must be satisfied if the source-market is to be cleared. Equation 7 requires that r_t be consistent with the stock of sources at t and the final-demand parameters (β).

The reader might be interested in Burstein's treatment of a similar model in analyzing the "machinery market" as part of a macroeconomic general-equilibrium model.[6]

The following system gives the full equilibrium solution of equations 1 through 7 in a stationary economy. In a system experiencing steady balanced growth (say at i^o), an equivalent system's solution would find S growing log-linearly with r steady.

(8) $$s_t = \Phi\,(p_t)$$

(9) $$d_t = kS_t$$

(10) $$S_t = \Psi\,(p_t,\ r_t,\ i_t^o)$$

(11) $$d_t = s_t$$

(12) $$r_t = f(S_t,\ \beta)$$

In a steady state, the subscript t can be dropped. In full equilibrium S_t is such that accumulation ceases; desired and actual stocks at t are identical. A crucial relationship exists between $\bar{r}$ and $\bar{p}$, given k and i^o. Returns from holding transportation sources will, in full equilibrium, permit a rate of return i^o on investment in transportation sources. Otherwise the stock of such sources will be growing or decaying.

---

[6]M. L. Burstein, *Money* (Cambridge, Mass.: Schenkman Publishing Co., 1963), pp. 591-592. The foundations of stock-flow analysis are set out at pp. 485-491, *loc. cit.*

We have delineated properties of solutions of simple competitive transportation industry models. Later we briefly shall take up efficiency properties. Now we try to confine ourselves to analysis of "positive" aspects, although the confines sometimes become unbearable.

The solution has at least the following implicit characteristics:

1. At no time can tariff differentials between hauls from A to B reflect anything but direct cost differentials so long as we can assume that equipment is unspecialized and *provided that equipment-rental costs are equal for alternative runs*. Competition among carriers and shippers assures this.

2. When $r = 0$ (in equilibrium r is the same for all), tariffs reflect nothing but direct costs, exclusive, of course, of equipment rental, postulated to be zero. Still, transitional "unjustified" differentials in tariffs might be necessary in order to bring about arbitrage.

3. When $r > 0$, there is implied a basic scarcity rent for equipment, assuring that nobody will be left on the platform who is willing to pay more than is anyone on the train for the same service.

4. Rents are defined so as to have a time dimension; rents are per diem, per month, etc. But the fact that a carrier pays $x per day for use of an outfit of equipment does not mean that a shipper from B to A will ordinarily pay the same rate as will a shipper from A to B under competition. This can be made clear through reference to a *two-site economy*. The "economic" traffic flow from Chicago to Dogpatch will much exceed that from Dogpatch to Chicago, perhaps reflecting transfer payments by Chicagoans with Dogpatch relatives. Taking up a *three-site economy,* if an outfit of equipment rented for $100 per day and a carrier had the dichotomous choice of using an outfit to go from A to B to A or from A to C to A, each round trip requiring one day, the decisive consideration, *cet. par.* would be attainable net revenues. If direct costs (sans equipment rentals) are the same for all legs, and if both activities are being undertaken, net profits will be the same in both activities. A-C, C-A traffic might be "balanced," so that tariffs from A to C are the same as those from C to A. A-B, B-A traffic might be unbalanced; the A-B tariff might much exceed the B-A tariff. Still there would be no incentive to under-

take arbitrage; anyone cutting the price from A to B would be unable to pay his equipment rental out of haulage proceeds.

5. Needless to say, when the choices of (4) become more varied, the rate structure becomes more complicated. Consider Figure One. Ignore direct expenses other than equipment rentals charged by source-owners to carriers. Assume that loading and unloading time is nil. Recall that r_t is a per diem rate determined in the source-rental market which is made by source-holders and carriers (haulers); r_t applies uniformly, quite independently of the application of a given source. The arrows indicate economic traffic flows. Assume that B-C, C-B traffic is balanced and of a lower order of magnitude than A-B or C-A traffic. If the triangle can be run in a day (and we assume that no greater distance can be traversed in a day) and if delivery times during the day are immaterial, quoted tariffs will be positive and equal for all but B-C (C-B) routings for which they will be zero. The opportunity cost of going from A to C, for example, is given by the tariff between A and B; an A-C trip requires that the carrier forego an A-B trip. On the other hand, if the B-C (C-B) tariff became positive, hoards of trucks would appear at B(C) docks seeking payloads; supply of shipping services quickly would exceed demand at these points.

6. An A-C routing, for example, must "compete" with an A-B-C route, evoking the obvious "simplex" criterion that for an activity to be used its direct cost must not exceed its indirect cost.[7] Thus, unless the tariff from A to C equalled that from A to B less fuel expense and the wage bill from B to C, anyone contemplating an A-C-A route could not compete with one contemplating an A-B-C-A route in the market made by haulers and source-owners. When fuel and wage costs are considered, equilibrium might even require that the tariff from A to C exceed that from C to A.

7. A thoroughly arbitraged tariff structure would, under the rather rigid assumptions of this model, have at least the following features:

---

[7]Needless to say, in equilibrium, included routes earn zero profits, while excluded routes offer negative profits. Excluded routes do not earn enough for carriers to be able to pay their rent.

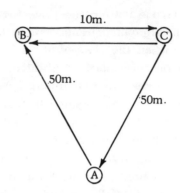

Figure One

a. Carriers contemplating A-B-A, A-B, C-A, etc. movements will expect equal profitability on all sequences actually employed.

b. The tariff from C to A (A to B) cannot exceed that from A to B (C to A) by more than the direct expense, without rental, of a standard B-C (C-B) shipment, always assuming that these expenses are a linear function of miles traversed.

c. Of course, if total revenues of A-B-C-A type routes exceed those of A-B-A type routes, we know in our simple model that C-A and A-B tariffs will be identical. Since all transportation outfits will be making a complete circuit each day, and since clockwise and counterclockwise traffic flows always will be of equal intensity, we know that identical supplies will be facing identical demands at B and C.

d. If traffic flows between A and B and between C and A are not identical, the symmetry of results thus far described breaks down. Thus, if capacity expands enough to accommodate putatively exceptionally large flows from C to A, the equilibrium tariff structure might require that the A-B tariff not exceed incremental fuel and labor costs.

Perhaps the single most significant characteristic of the "equilibrium" competitive rate structures delineated here is that, while daily rates paid for identical perfectly mobile outfits would be the same for all carriers, shadow rents assessed by carriers once they have hired the outfits would vary a great deal for runs of equal duration. Efficient utilization of transportation capacities requires that tariffs be sensitive to a host of specifications including the time of the day, week, or month, location of terminals, consonance with other trips, etc.[8] Solution of the *back-haul problem* requires a highly sensitive pricing mechanism.[9]

This leads to analysis of the general n-point multiperiod horizon case and, less directly, to Section 3.3. If the transportation industry attains intertemporal efficiency,[10] what might be thought of as a transition matrix governing the movement of rolling stock and cargos will be efficient. Think of it this way. A stroboscope flashes regularly. Over a complete cycle, each flash finds the transportation stock in a different phase. The relevant alternatives to equipment being at point i at date t can be described only in space-time. No general solution appears to exist for this analogue to the Multidimensional Trans-

---

[8]The text's argument has not taken up the role of *freight-forwarding*. Freight forwarders, among other things, perform as arbitragers, and characteristically sublease sources from carriers. Exercise of their role makes sure that items making up cargos for cars and trailers are selected so that costs are minimized, although they also assure that shippers willing to pay premiums for speedier transits are accommodated. In a purely competitive market, one could not be sure what *differential* tariffs would be charged at t for shipment of Product X_r as against Product X_s; all would depend on cargo alignments at that time. There might be heavy shipments of steel but very little movement of produce; an exigent strawberry shipper might have to pay a huge premium in order to have his berries taken along with a shipment of I-beams—unless he could outbid steel shippers for the entire car, in which case his rental *per cubic foot mile* would be less. Protection against such contingencies would have to be bought in futures markets. Doubtless "insurance" would be inexpensive, especially since developing patterns of future requirements would induce speculators to cover shippers' positions.

[9]The over-all constraints require that proposed utilizations at t not exceed capacities at t. Capacities must also be defined in terms of availabilities at each location.

[10]For elucidation of general concepts of intertemporal efficiency, see R. Dorfman, P. Samuelson, and R. Solow, *Linear Programming and Economic Analysis* (New York: McGraw-Hill Book Co., 1958), Ch. 12, especially pp. 309-322. It should be stressed that in the text's problem, firms are "choosing" parameters of transitions matrixes in response to market-determined tariff structures.

portation Problem.[11] One sees that, as more alternatives are introduced, however, the tariff structure tends to exhibit less drastic differentials; alternatives such as going from Dogpatch to Allentown to New York to Pittsburgh to Akron to Detroit to Chicago might be revenue producing as against the barren Dogpatch-Chicago possibility of our two-point case.

3.3 EFFICIENCY AND WELFARE

Perhaps the New Welfare Economics has slit its throat with Occam's Razor.[12] Fortunately, however, we are concerned with efficiency questions at the micro level and are able to deal with cardinal criterion functions. Nor do "Second Best" issues intrude upon us. Agreed that, if the social marginal cost of a rail transit from A to B is $0.10, of a truck transit $0.20 and the regulated rail tariff $0.50, free competition in the trucking industry undoubtedly will lead to disuse of the socially less expensive method. But here we deal with criteria of firms facing given external transportation tariffs; we are not called upon to evaluate the social properties of these external tariffs.

Our fairly considerable development of properties of competitive-equilibrium states could be seriously misleading. It would be extraordinary if a competitive industry were in either short- or long-run equilibrium at t. Thus if the vector $\bar{p}(t)$ were a vector of efficient prices, and if the competitive solution vector also were $\bar{p}(t)$, we still might be far from home. The r-th price can be expected to behave according to a dynamic law such as

$$(13) \qquad \dot{p}_r = f(d_r - s_r).$$

If $p_r(t\text{-}h) \neq \bar{p}_r(t)$, $p_r(t)$ usually will deviate from $\bar{p}_r(t)$. Indeed, as institutional and historical siege guns are brought up, the likelihood of $p_r(t) = \bar{p}_r(t)$ appears to be slight. We must not permit

---

[11]Compare S. I. Gass, *Linear Programming* (New York: McGraw-Hill Book Co., 1958), pp. 178-179.

Operations Research, Vol. 11, No. 1 (Jan.-Feb. 1963) contains a report of related work at p. 169, specifically, a thesis by Robert F. Miller, "An Analysis of a Motor Freight Scheduling Problem," at The Ohio State University, 1961.

[12]Arnold Harberger's phrase.

writers to invoke, say, uncertainty and evolution to claim that, because competitive prices at t are tending towards $\bar{p}(t)$, competitive market structures at t necessarily yield efficient constellations of prices and outputs.

The pieces begin to fit together. The theory of efficient allocation of resources and the practice of fiat transportation tariffs and alternative market structures lead to the same outcome: firms are encouraged to provide their own carriage. The analysis is *not* peculiarly centered on effects of rate setting by fiat; the very complexity of properties of *equilibrium* competitive rate structures encourages belief that ongoing processes at t will depart in important ways from efficient sets at t.

The preponderant role of the theory of welfare economics at this stage of the analysis is not surprising: the conventional criterion function of the firm is nicely cardinal; maximization of present value does not incite teleological controversy. For the firm, economic efficiency is unambiguous and usually requires a unique program. Still the analysis is practically identical with that of general welfare theory: the firm necessarily is selecting a point on an efficient frontier.

Thus, theoretical analysis suggests strong incentive for vertical integration to embrace motor transport and, indeed, suggests that efficiency criteria call for vertical integration in many areas not ordinarily thought of in that connection.[13] Attention again is called to the dangers of identifying equilibrium tariffs with actual tariffs. The latter, as elementary dynamical analysis verifies, can markedly differ from the former for long intervals of time even in purely competitive markets.

3.4 EMPIRICAL WORK

To repeat, we examined data pertaining to a large wholesale grocer operating private motor carriage on intercity hauls throughout the United States. Our procedures and basic results are described in this section. The terminal points included Chicago, Detroit, Indianapolis,

---

[13]*Cf.* M. L. Burstein, "The Economics of Tie-In Sales," *Review of Economics and Statistics*, Feb. 1960, and "A Theory of Full-Line Forcing," *Northwestern University Law Review*, Mar.-Apr., 1960.

New York, San Francisco, Atlanta, Dallas, Pittsburgh, and Philadelphia. The estimates are based on 1960-1961 experience. First, estimates of direct cost are developed. Then successive approximations are undertaken. Finally, comparisons can be made with published rates and various profitability estimates can be attempted.

Payroll data and questionnaire response revealed running times from one point to another and permitted calculation of in-transit labor and fuel expense. Loading and unloading costs similarly were developed. There are seven other categories of tractor expense that were worked into direct-cost estimates:

a. hours of maintenance labor;
b. oil;
c. miscellaneous repair expense on the road;
d. repairs, parts, tires, and maintenance "purchased";
e. insurance;
f. Federal Use Tax;
g. driver time paid during breakdowns and repairs.

Sources of these data were (where [a] is source of "hours of maintenance labor")

a. Company garage reports and personnel department information on wage rates, including fringe benefits and payroll taxes;
b. trip sheets made out by each driver;
c. files kept by company for each piece of equipment;
d. the company's insurance department;
e. the company's tax records;
f. drivers' time cards.

The company's accounting procedures called for these "other" categories of expense to be cumulated to the account of each of its five tractors. Its records also showed how many miles each tractor traveled over each year. It becomes easy to calculate expected "other" costs per mile, and, once one knows distances between terminals, "other" costs can be converted into trip costs.

The foregoing appears to be an unexceptionable procedure for handling oil expenditures. As for items (a), (c)-(g), our procedure is based on postulation of a rectangular probability-density function:

116

the expected value of (d), for example, on a trip of x miles is ½ that of a trip of 2x miles.

Procedures just like those used for tractors were also used to obtain imputations for the following expenses associated with the company's nineteen trailers. Sources are as above.

a. hours of maintenance labor
b. repairs, parts, tires, and maintenance "purchased"
c. insurance

Seven categories of labor expense required imputation:

a. payments to union health and welfare funds;
b. payments to the union pension fund;
c. six and one-half paid holidays;
d. vacation pay;
e. Workmen's Compensation insurance;
f. unemployment compensation tax;
g. Social Security tax

The sources of the data employed were the union contract and sundry company personnel and insurance records. The imputational procedure was extremely careful. Each driver's annual fringe benefits and other costs (thus, the unemployment-compensation tax was $30.00 per man) were recorded. When trips required tandem drivers, the precise sums appropriate to the respective teams were employed. Finally, it became possible to estimate imputed costs (fringe benefits, etc.) per driver pay mile for individual trips and per tandem pay mile for each of the tandems that might be employed.

Loading and unloading cost estimates already referred to above were developed through rather elaborate procedures, although, unfortunately, rents were not imputed to lift trucks.

The first step found us estimating the time it would normally take to load and unload the company's trailers under various circumstances. In truth, the regressions (all estimation was based on minimization of sums of squared deviations from linear regression equations) were applied only to *un*loading times. The company's industrial engineer's studies convinced him that loading time for the j-th shipment would be expected to be 80 per cent of unloading time.

117

Eight regression equations were estimated in connection with the company's experience in unloading its own trucks:

i.	$y_{11} = a_{01} + a_{11}x_1 + a_{21}x_2 + a_{31}x_3 + u_1$
ii.	$y_{11} = a_{02} + a_{12}x_1 + a_{22}x_2 + u_2$
iii.	$y_{21} = a_{03} + a_{13}x_1 + u_3$
iv.	$y_{11} = a_{04} + a_{24}x_2 + u_4$
v.	$y_{12} = a_{05} + a_{15}x_1 + a_{25}x_2 + a_{35}x_3 + u_5$
vi.	$y_{12} = a_{06} + a_{16}x_1 + a_{26}x_2 + u_6$
vii.	$y_{22} = a_{07} + a_{17}x_1 + u_7$
viii.	$y_{12} = a_{08} + a_{28}x_2 + u_8$

In the expression y_{ij}, i indexes "canned goods and chemicals" and j "without and with forklift truck." Thus y_{11} concerns canned-goods cargos unloaded without the aid of lift trucks; y_{22}, chemical cargos unloaded with forklift trucks. The y's measure hours of labor. As for included independent variables: $x_1 = $ weight of shipment; $x_2 = $ number of pieces in shipment; $x_3 = $ number of items (goods classifications) in shipment. The regressions were run on data collected from March to June, 1961 [14]

Next, similar regression analysis was conducted for loading and unloading of railroad cars (common-carrier trucks performed these operations as part of the service under published rates). It thus became possible to obtain fully comparable expense experience for rail-carriage alternatives to private carriage.

Labor time was costed for each of the nine company terminals according to prevailing rates on 1 January, 1961. Fringe benefits and payroll taxes were included in labor costs. Hourly rates (including fringe benefits and payroll taxes) ranged from $2.664 at Dallas to $3.584 at New York, but it still was assumed that productivity was the same at each entrepot.[15]

In-transit labor and fuel expenses were referred to earlier. These were, of course, the easiest cost elements to estimate. Cost records

---

[14] Tests of significance on multiple and partial correlation coefficients led us to use regression ii to estimate canned-goods loading and unloading times and to use regression iii for chemicals. The partials were significant beyond the .025 level.

[15] An *average* productivity.

and questionnaires provided expected fuel consumptions, mileage taxes, tolls, expense allowances to drivers for overnight stays, driver wages (including per mile and per hour elements), etc. Hundreds of trips were used in our estimates.

It finally is possible to display the results. A group of 9 x 9 matrices appears to be a successful device. The designations are: (A), Chicago; (B), Detroit; (C), Indianapolis; (D), Long Island City; (E), San Francisco; (F), Atlanta; (G), Dallas; (H), Pittsburgh; (I), Philadelphia.

First a matrix of mean weights and mean numbers-of-pieces, followed by the number of observations—in that order—for canned-goods movements (which will be taken up first).

Matrix a, Weights and Pieces—Canned Goods

		A	B	C	D	E	F	G	H	I
					DESTINATION					
O R I G I N	A		25864 734 14	28002 .891 49	36800 912 4	41057 975 14			30857 766 7	28700 920 1
	B	32410 625 10								
	C	32744 812 160	30368 790 22		36375 937 44	40553 1013 2	32300 791 7		32240 818 10	33500 914 9
	D	35692 1060 25	33421 897 11	32700 710 2					31600 890 1	
	E	40900 900 1								
	F									
	G									
	H		32300 750 1		30800 810 1					
	I				17300 282 4					

119

There follows a matrix of mean driving-times and pay-miles.

Matrix b, Driving Times and Pay-Miles—Canned Goods

		DESTINATION								
		A	B	C	D	E	F	G	H	I
O R I G I N	A	hours miles	8.14 301	5.06 200	21.25 900	24.93 2258			13.14 497	18.00 900
	B	8.30 309								
	C	5.05 202	8.77 306		20.06 862	60.00 2493	16.14 579		13.00 466	18.89 818
	D	21.24 885	16.27 691	21.00 880					13.00 540	
	E	55.00 2250								
	F									
	G									
	H		7.00 290		9.00 480					
	I				3.25 100					

The next step is to display what we term "mean running costs."
These are based on in-transit labor and fuel expenses. Loading and
unloading expenses and the imputed costs described earlier are excluded. As was pointed out in Sections 3.1 and 3.2, Matrix c, together
with Matrix d (below), give rise to rock-bottom competitive rates
during periods of excess capacity *so long as labor inputs can be
considered variable in the short run.*

Matrix c, Mean Running Costs—Canned Goods

		DESTINATION								
		A	B	C	D	E	F	G	H	I
O R I G I N	A		53.37	36.08	213.37	457.59			107.94	188.79
	B	60.96								
	C	33.79	52.92		235.83	460.42	134.13		83.73	179.58
	D	229.71	170.84	192.38					103.41	
	E	438.66								
	F									
	G									
	H		63.74		98.13					
	I				35.64					

The regressions referred to earlier for loading and unloading costs lead to Matrix d.

Matrix d, Mean Loading and Unloading Costs—Canned Goods

		DESTINATION								
		A	B	C	D	E	F	G	H	I
	A		$14.95	15.64	22.54	23.83			18.32	18.02
	B	15.73								
	C	16.55	15.72		20.93	22.13	14.80		17.97	17.83
	D	23.81	20.93	16.14					21.58	
	E	22.63								
	F									
	G									
	H		18.48		20.11					
	I				6.69					

We quickly proceed to present the sums of costs pertaining to tractors, trailers, and drivers, imputed to the respective hauls. Following procedures described earlier, these imputations were reduced to a per-mile basis. . . . Needless to say, the *pièce de résistance* is the matrix of mean direct costs displayed in Matrix f.

Matrix e, Mean Imputed (But "Direct") Costs—Canned Goods

	A	B	C	D	E	F	G	H	I
A		$25.37	19.09	96.66	233.48			35.81	95.40
B	30.12								
C	19.17	30.77		81.39	261.25	49.23		41.09	78.40
D	79.87	71.32	81.61						
E	211.50								
F									
G									
H		23.20		28.80					
I				10.50					

Matrix f, Mean Direct Costs, simply is the sum of Matrices c through e.

Matrix f, Mean Direct Costs—Canned Goods

	A	B	C	D	E	F	G	H	I
A		$ 93.69	70.81	332.57	714.90			162.07	302.21
B	106.81								
C	69.51	99.41		338.15	743.80	198.16		142.79	275.81
D	333.39	263.09	290.13					164.41	
E	672.79								
F									
G									
H		105.42		147.04					
I				52.83					

Matrix g provides a truncated-matrix of external alternative costs and "savings" (g-f). External tariffs are calculated on the basis of information supplied by one of the company's servants. They show what the company would have had to pay for indicated truckload or carload hauls in December, 1960. The fact that the company did not *consider* public motor carriage for hauls to San Francisco hampers our work, although study of the chemical cases largely offsets this. External alternatives always are adjusted so as to provide for loading-and-unloading expenses. Thus the portal-to-portal characteristics of the internal and external opportunities are identical. (Differences are computed against motor carriage when possible; rail tariffs are marked "R.")

Matrix g, External-Alternative Costs; Differences (g-f)—Canned Goods

		DESTINATIONS							
		A	B	C	D	E	F	H	I
O R I G I N	A		160. 36 66. 67	112.01 41. 20	368. 56(R) 574. 08 241. 51	781. 34(R) 66. 44		244. 20(R) 249. 94 87. 87	350. 40(R) 427. 63 125. 42
	B	249. 56 142. 75	motor alternative difference						
	C								
	D	342. 64 9. 25	280. 79 17. 70	294. 30 4. 17				214. 88 50. 47	
	E	706. 71(R) 748. 47 75. 68							
	F								
	H		274. 55 169. 13		215. 60 68. 56				
	I				136. 80 83. 97				

It remains to complete the "profitability" analysis. But first we turn to "chemicals."

We wish to build a structure for chemical (largely dry and liquid wash compounds mostly shipped in fibre containers) shipments comparable to that built up for canned goods. The analysis is confined largely to movements from Detroit (B). We confine ourselves to showing mean running costs (equivalent to Matrix c), mean direct costs (equivalent to Matrix f), and the counterpart to Matrix g.

Matrix h, Mean Running Costs, Mean Direct Costs
(= MRC + Imputed Elements),
Common Carrier Truck Rates, Differences for Chemicals(s)
Shipment from Detroit to Other Points, 1960

	Chicago	Indianapolis	Long Is. Cty.	Atlanta	Dallas	Pittsburgh
MRC	$ 52.54	50.73	129.53	155.35	186.39	59.77
MDC	97.94	86.76	192.51	231.31	294.81	94.43
CCTrR	116.68	100.20	276.64	362.97	685.84	170.01
Diff.	18.74	22.44	84.13	131.48	391.03	75.58

We cannot reach conclusion until general-overhead and capital-expense items are taken into account.

As for *general overhead,* it appears that a $14,000 per annum rate is roughly correct. This includes $11,900 per annum worth of the time of salaried employees and $2,100 in other expenses. Office space can be ignored as a consideration. Since the company maintains considerable garaging facilities for its intracity hauls, and particularly since servicing activities largely are concentrated in Chicago using facilities necessary for Chicago intracity operations, garage facilities also can be ignored.

Capital costs—here interest and depreciation—prove much more significant to the analysis than do general overhead expenses. Private-carriage activities are broken-down into two categories: activities sufficiently "regular" to be considered to tie-up one or more "outfits"

124

of equipment; "irregular" activities for which capital expenses cannot be computed so simply. An outfit of equipment can be taken to consist of two trailers and one tractor and, depending on the complexity of the equipment, can be valued at $20 to $30 thousand (when purchased new). The appropriate straight-line depreciation rate appears to be about 15 per cent; depreciation expense varies from $3,000 to $4,500 per annum per outfit.

As for interest, a 10 per cent rate of return on average balances might be appropriate. Thus interest expense for a $30,000 outfit in its first year of operation would be $2,800. That for a $20,000 outfit would be $1,800. It becomes apparent that the straight-line depreciation assumption cannot hold up under rigorous analysis: it would pay the carrier (private or otherwise) to hold only the most aged equipment or to rent equipment (rents of new and old equipment being implicitly equal under straight line assumptions) if straight-line depreciation were applicable. We shall squirm out of these troubles simply by assuming that the optimal equipment mix finds market values of representative outfits of $10,000 to $15,000, continuing to use straight-line depreciation. Interest expense per complete outfit will then be from $1,000 to $1,500 per annum. No fixed capital other than rolling stock need be considered.

"Regular" activities, one tying-up one tractor and two trailers, the other (SF) but one trailer, included round-trip canned-goods transits from Chicago to Indianapolis and Chicago to San Francisco. The former involved 104 round trips a year, the latter 52 round trips per year.

Taking up the Chicago-Indianapolis-Chicago canned-goods activity, noting that back-haul is assured (a crucial matter in private-carriage decisions from the point of the firm which might be hedged-in by a wide variety of restrictions unless it can generate its own back-hauls), and relying on Matrix g, we see that "gross" profitability is $160 per week, $8,300 per annum. Annual capital costs cannot possibly exceed $6,000 per annum and, in this instance, are more likely to be $4,000 per annum. Needless to say, the general overhead item should not be taken up here if indeed it can be taken as an irreducible lump of expense to be associated with the decision of the company to engage in private carriage. It should be considered only "at the end" when the over-all decision whether or not to "exit" is made.[16]

As for the Chicago-San Francisco-Chicago activity, Matrix g suggests that its "gross" profitability is approximately $140 per week (the back-haul is assured), $7,300 per annum. Annual capital costs for this run (using sleeper cabs, etc.) can more sensibly be taken to be $4,100. Both of these "regular" activities appear to be highly profitable.

The "irregular" trips pose particularly difficult problems. Here, we cannot work with fixed outfits of equipment. Instead we deal with a pool of roughly 2 tractors (supplemented by 2 standby tractors) and 14 trailers, utilized over the entire country. Capital costs for these irregular operations (we ignore the fact that equipment sometimes is shunted from regular runs in order to accommodate irregular activities) are roughly $18,000 per annum. ($13,500 proves to be recovered through Chicago-Detroit-Chicago and Chicago-Long Island City-Chicago activities, covering about 40 per cent of irregular activity.)

It is difficult to make specific assertions about "irregular" activities (trips). Thus, consider a shipment of chemicals from Detroit to Dallas. Matrix h shows that the gross profitability of this one-way haul is about $390. If the equipment pool is specified as in the foregoing quite independently of Detroit-Dallas activity, and if the Detroit-

---

[16]Needless to say, in making the ultimate judgment of the profitability of private carriage, depreciation charges on the *entire fleet* (assumed here to be optimal), together with interest charges on invested capital, will be used. Aggregate capital expense, considering the entire array of equipment, is about $30,000 per annum (based, as is the study, on 1960 operations). Add to this the $14,000 general overhead expense; the sum of "fixed" expense to be recovered is, then, $44,000 (per annum). The Chicago-Indianapolis and Chicago-San Francisco canned-goods haulage activities alone have been shown in the text to contribute about $15,600 to the "offset." Matrices g and h make clear that the remaining activities easily should be able to absorb the remaining $28,400 of the "nut." As it happens, this study is not seriously concerned with the "exit" decision of the company. Obviously, scale economies will exist at *some* level . . . Our hunch is that, if other private-carriage activities were abandoned, so that total capital costs would be about $8,000 per annum, it is almost certain that the true irreducible lump of overhead would be less than $7,600. Obviously scale economies are very low in motor haulage.

Dallas haul can be timed to coincide with an over-all schedule that would find a tractor and trailer idle, it is obvious that the Detroit-Dallas activity is gravy. Indeed, if the trip were to occur once a year, there would appear to be no reason to make alternative specifications, although it would be important to consider the expense of moving the equipment from Dallas to another point *if* Dallas were incapable of generating back-haul traffic.

It would appear that the irregular activities suggest two basic queries:

a. is the total gross profitability of these activities, taken collectively, sufficient to justify employment of the capital now engaged? If not, is there some other set of irregular activities that would justify employment of *some* capital?
b. is a particular irregular activity justified, considering the capital that might be dispensed with if this activity is abandoned?

One suspects that moderate assumptions about flexibilities in timing of deliveries assure that the answer to (b) almost always will be "yes," even for very modest gross profitabilities: it should be relatively simple to work out a schedule over the year finding the equipment shunting over the country, always in operation, the activities nicely meshed. On the other hand, the answer to (a) could well be "no" even when that to (b) is emphatically "yes." The short-run marginal costs, so to speak, of each activity might be zero, while "the last dollar's worth of capital" is failing to achieve satisfactory returns.

Finally, attention should be called to the accounting scheme that has been employed and which appears to conform to criteria suggested by economic theory. The accounting scheme has recognized two distinct types of decisions: (a) decisions as to how to employ a predetermined aggregation of capital at t; (b) decisions as to the optimal set of capital equipment when the firm is fully adjusted. Type (a) decision criteria were formulated so as to avoid consideration of any but truly direct costs. Type (b) decision criteria were formulated so that the decision unit could compare maximum gross profitabilities for a wide range of capital sets, choosing that capital set which, for example, achieved equilibration of the marginal internal rate of return with the appropriate external rate of return. In the case of our company, it is clear that rational behavior called for it to operate substantial private-carriage activity.

3.5 CONCLUSION

Section 3.1 already has developed the major inferences we have drawn from the work reported in this paper. This section cites detailed quantitative support for these inferences. Specifically it is shown that: (i) published rates do not accurately reflect direct cost differentials; (ii) these discrepancies are relatively larger for longer hauls; (iii) the calculations of Section 3.4 have special interest for analysis of motor-carriage tariffs, including inferences about plausible "free" tariff structures.

As for points (i) and (ii), consult Matrices f-h, noting that Section 3.4 suggested that capital-cost differentials for motor-carriage activities were not crucial (i.e. for activities only differing spatially). It becomes clear that regulated differentials have an irregular relationship with cost differences: the very wide range of the "bottom" entries in Matrix g, for example, is decisive. And, most certainly, our results jibe with a common belief about regulated trucking: long-distance hauls are the more profitable.

As for (iii), it is obvious that *all* of the hauls analyzed here would be what we have called "regular activities" in an unregulated transportation industry. And, of course, these hauls are "regular" for common carriers and others at this time. It follows that Section 3.4: calculations provide basis for obtaining direct and capital costs for transportation activities. We have shown that scale economies are not significant; the data seem best to be explained by scaling up unit-activity costs, the costs of using an outfit of equipment from A(B) to B(A).[17]

---

[17]The text in Section 3.4 briefly considered motor-carriage patterns in n-point economies in which there were movements more complicated than the A-B-A movements stressed here. Of course, "n-point" considerations suggest that our cost estimates are biased upward.

128

It is true that freight rates would have to permit return of more than what we have called *direct* and *capital* costs: *general overhead* costs (*cf.* Sec. 3.4) must be recovered. General-overhead costs could not, we argued, rigorously be imputed to specific activities. It follows that the "basic rate" applying to a fictional activity not requiring direct costs will somewhat exceed associated capital costs.

Again it should be emphasized that capital costs are defined as time rates, while direct costs are defined as "lumps" associated with transits. The problem to be "solved" by the market is to determine how much capital should be diverted to the *i-th* activity. In the course of this determination, the level of rents will become determined. In a competitive market, tariff differentials would be determined, *cet. par.*, by direct-cost differentials associated with hauling Cargo X instead of Cargo Y. Profitabilities would be equal.

If haulage of Cargo X reduced the number of trips that can be made per period (as against haulage of Cargo Y), the activities should be separated in the analysis. In general, each cargo will entail different capital costs for standard hauls (A-B); amounts of working capital would have to be tied up at t in order for ton-mile-per-period rates for Cargos X and Y to be equal. A colorful example compares haulage of dynamite with that of canned goods.

Finally, it would be easy for carriers to compute what we have called "capital costs" in a world of perfect markets: source-owners would lease outfits of equipment at standardized rates. Carriers, in quoting to shippers, would need but to calculate the rent they must pay to source-owners if they were to ship Cargo X from A to B. In the short run, these rents would be subject to what might be very substantial fluctuation. (See Sec. 3.2, for some back-haul problems.)

One final comment. Our approach to cost analysis has been highly disaggregated. Our concern has been as much with the structure as with *the* level of rates. Our work suggests that cost studies associating ton-mile-per-period outputs with dollar-valued rates of input utilization should be handled with no little caution.

129

Appendix*

Underlying and Supplementary Data and Data Processing

I. Regressions Used in the Estimation of Loading and Unloading Costs: Supplement to Matrix d.

  A. The Company's Loading and Unloading Times.

  1. The Regression Equations

i. $$y_{11} = a_{01} + a_{11}x_1 + a_{21}x_2 + a_{31}x_3 + u_1$$

ii. $$y_{11} = a_{02} + a_{12}x_1 + a_{22}x_2 + u_2$$

iii. $$y_{21} = a_{03} + a_{13}x_1 + u_3$$

iv. $$y_{11} = a_{04} + a_{24}x_2 + u_4$$

v. $$y_{12} = a_{05} + a_{15}x_1 + a_{25}x_2 + a_{35}x_3 + u_5$$

vi. $$y_{12} = a_{06} + a_{16}x_1 + a_{26}x_2 + u_6$$

vii. $$y_{22} = a_{07} + a_{17}x_1 + u_7$$

viii. $$y_{12} = a_{08} + a_{28}x_2 + u_8$$

y_{ij} = hours of labor, with $i = \begin{cases} 1, \text{for canned goods} \\ 2, \text{for chemicals} \end{cases}$, $j = \begin{cases} 1, \text{without lift truck} \\ 2, \text{with lift truck} \end{cases}$;

a_{oj} = y-axis intercept, where the "j" refers to the particular equation;

a_{ij} = regression coefficient for the i-*th* variable of the j-*th* equation;

u_j = residual error term for the j-*th* equation;

x_1 = weight of shipment;

x_2 = number of pieces in shipment;

x_3 = number of items in shipment.

2. Results of the Regression Equations

  a. Original Results.

---

*Prepared by E. Glustoff.

TABLE 3.1. General Results of the Regression Equations.

#	n	R^2	r	σ_e	range/σ_e	Intercept	F-Test
i.	53	.51	.72	1.346	4.56	-0.667	1%
ii.	53	.49	.70	1.356	4.65	-0.573	1%
iii.	53	.46	.68	1.385	4.48	-0.498	1%
iv.	53	.46	.68	1.386	4.44	-0.220	1%
v.	53	.53	.73	1.714	4.21	-0.717	1%
vi.	53	.52	.72	1.720	4.32	-0.615	1%
vii.	53	.50	.70	1.750	4.20	-0.527	1%
viii.	53	.48	.69	1.780	4.12	-0.082	1%

where

      # = equation number;

      n = sample size;

      R^2 = coefficient of determination;

      r = correlation coefficient;

      σ_e = standard error of estimate

  range/σ_e = range of residuals divided by the standard error of estimate;

  intercept = a_{0i} = y-axis intercept;

and the entries in the column headed "F-Test" refer to the level at which the computed F-value was significant, with a single-tailed F-test.

TABLE 3.2. Results of the Variables of the Regression Equations for the Variables.

	x_1				x_2				x_3			
	b	σ_b	T	r_b	b	σ_b	T	r_b	b	σ_b	T	r_b
i.	.00007	.00003	2.5%	.288	.00133	.00144	20%	.131	.02574	.01937	10%	.186
ii.	.00006	.00003	2.5%	.247	.00228	.00127	2.5%	.247				
iii.	.00011	.00002	0.5%	——								
iv.					.00426	.00064	0.5%	——				
v.	.00010	.00004	2.5%	.322	.00163	.00184	20%	.125	.02800	.02468	10%	.161
vi.	.00009	.00004	2.5%	.291	.00266	.00160	10%	.228				
vii.	.00015	.00002	0.5%	——								
viii.					.00565	.00083	0.5%	——				
MEAN	$\bar{x}_1 = 27,054$				$\bar{x}_2 = 672$				$\bar{x}_3 = 2.6$			

  b = the regression coefficient;

  σ_b = the standard error of the regression coefficient;

  T = the level at which the computed t-value was significant; as a single-tailed test;

  r_b = partial correlation coefficient

Because the intercepts were negative, a situation with no economic significance for this problem, it was decided to divide the sample in two parts and run separate sets of regressions. The sample was split according to whether or not a shipment was greater than 23,000 pounds.

b. Second Regressions

TABLE 3.3. Shipments with More Than 23,000 Pounds.

	n	R^2	r	σ_e	Intercept	F
i.	36	.08	.28	1.540	0.090	*
ii.	36	.08	.27	1.520	0.341	*
iii.	36	.07	.26	1.501	0.397	*
iv.	36	.04	.20	1.524	2.084	*
v.	36	.10	.31	1.933	0.055	*
vi.	36	.10	.31	1.904	0.211	*
vii.	36	.09	.30	1.878	0.256	*
viii.	36	.04	.21	1.933	3.050	*

*indicates that the F-value was not significant at the 5 per cent level on a one-tail test.

TABLE 3.4. Variable Results of Shipments of More Than 23,000 Pounds.

	x_1		x_2		x_3	
	b	σ_b	b	σ_b	b	σ_b
i.	.00008	.00007	.00048	.00188	.00935	.02528
ii.	.00008	.00007	.00073	.00172		
iii.	.00009	.00006				
iv.			.00175	.00145		
v.	.00013	.00009	.00042	.00235	.00582	.03173
vi.	.00012	.00009	.00058	.00216		
vii.	.00014*	00007				
viii.			.00225	.00148		

*indicates significant under a one-tail t-test at the 5 per cent level.

TABLE 3.5. Regression Results for Shipments with less than 23,000.

	n	R	r	σ_e	Intercept	F
i.	14	.85	.93	0.084	0.094	1%
ii.	14	.84	.92	0.379	0.131	1%
iii.	14	.22	.46	0.814	-0.245	*
iv.	14	.76	.87	0.448	-0.354	1%
v.	14	.84	.92	0.521	0.470	1%
vi.	14	.83	.91	0.516	0.523	1%
vii.	14	.16	.41	1.095	0.018	*
viii.	14	.71	.84	0.642	-0.235	1%

*indicates not significant at the 5% level.

TABLE 3.6. Results of the Variables for Shipments of less than 23,000.

	x_1		x_2		x_3	
	b	σ_b	b	σ_b	b	σ_b
i.	-.00007	.00004	.00409*	.00128	.01757	.02075
ii.	-.00008*	.00003	.00496*	.00075		
iii.	.00009*	.00005				
iv.			.00362*	.00058		
v.	-.00011	.00005	.00543*	.00174	.02473	.02816
vi.	-.00013*	.00005	.00666*	.00101		
vii.	.00100	.00006				
viii.			.00456	.00084		

B. Common Motor Carriers Loading and Unloading Time.
  1. The Regression Equations

i. $\qquad y_1 = a_{01} + a_{11}x_1 + a_{21}x_2 + a_{31}x_3 + u_1$

ii. $\qquad y_1 = a_{02} + a_{12}x_1 + a_{22}x_2 \qquad\quad + u_2$

iii. $\qquad y_1 = a_{03} + a_{13}x_1 \qquad\qquad\quad\ + u_3$

iv. $\qquad y_1 = a_{04} \qquad\quad + a_{24}x_2 \qquad\quad + u_4$

v. $\qquad y_2 = a_{05} + a_{15}x_1 + a_{25}x_2 + a_{35}x_3 + u_5$

vi. $\qquad y_2 = a_{06} + a_{16}x_1 + a_{26}x_2 \qquad\quad + u_6$

vii. $\qquad y_2 = a_{07} + a_{17}x_1 \qquad\qquad\quad\ + u_7$

viii. $\qquad y_2 = a_{08} \qquad\quad + a_{28}x_2 \qquad\quad + u_8$

where

$\quad y_1 =$ time to unload common carrier by an employee of the company,

$\quad y_2 =$ time to unload common carrier by an employee of the common carrier; the other variables are the same as before.

2. Estimated Regressions

TABLE 3.7

	n	R^2	r	σ_e	Intercept	F	b_1	b_2	b_3
i.	92	.26	.51	0.701	0.053	1%	+.00004	−.00031	.01304
ii.	92	.25	.50	0.704	0.020	1%	.00004	−.00002	
iii.	92	.25	.50	0.700	0.019	1%	.00004		
iv.	92	.19	.43	0.728	0.198	1%		.00135	
v.	92	.40	.63	1.059	0.089	1%	.00006	.00055	.02859
vi.	92	.37	.61	1.075	0.015	1%	.00005	.00120	
vii.	92	.36	.60	1.080	0.084	1%	.00008		
viii.	92	.33	.58	1.102	0.256	1%		.00305	

C. Regression Equations for Railroad Car Unloading Times.

I. The equations are the same as above expect that i-iv exclude lift trucks while v-viii include them.

D. Estimated Regressions.

TABLE 3.8. Regression Results for Unloading Railroad Cars.

	n	R^2	r	σ_e	Intercept	F	b_1	b_2	b_3
i.	35	.65	.81	1.710	0.117	1%	.00003	.00421	.011503
ii.	35	.62	.79	1.756	0.667	1%	.00003	.00453	
iii.	35	.44	.67	2.096	4.002	1%	.00009		
iv.	35	.60	.77	1.785	0.973	1%		.00576	
v.	35	.70	.83	1.950	-.031	1%	.00004	.00525	.16747
vi.	35	.65	.81	2.052	0.770	1%	.00004	.00572	
vii.	35	.47	.68	2.513	4.975	1%	.00012		
viii.	35	.63	.79	2.094	2.094	1%		.00723	

where

b_i = the regression coefficient for the i-th variable

II. Supplement to Matrix e.

TABLE 3.9. Matrix of Imputed Costs to Tractors.

	A	B	C	D	E	F	G	H	I
A	–	$14.49	11.52	63.20	163.88			21.62	71.10
B	19.78								
C	10.95	18.71	–	52.80	183.17	28.66		23.05	50.19
D	53.98	44.32	50.96					22.14	
E	153.00								
H		10.15		16.80					
I				7.35					

The city codes for the origin of shipments are the rows, while the destination city codes are the columns. The codes are:

A = Chicago   D = Long Island City   G = Dallas
B = Detroit   E = San Francisco   H = Pittsburgh
C = Indianapolis   F = Atlanta   I = Philadelphia

TABLE 3.10. Matrix of Imputed Costs to Trailers.

	A	B	C	D	E	F	G	H	I
A		7. 84	5. 42	21. 71	37. 23			9. 41	13. 50
B	7. 08								
C	6. 16	8. 65		18. 70	36. 45	14. 33		13. 10	19. 49
D	15. 48	18. 74	22. 70					11. 88	
E	24. 75								
H		6. 96		7. 20					
I				1. 80					

TABLE 3.11. Matrix of Imputed Costs to Drivers.

	A	B	C	D	E	F	G	H	I
A		3. 04	2. 15	11. 75	32. 37			4. 78	10. 80
B	3. 26								
C	2. 06	3. 41		9. 89	41. 63	6. 24		4. 94	8. 72
D	10. 41	8. 26	7. 95					5. 40	
E	33. 75								
H		6. 09		4. 80					
I				1. 35					

III. Supplement to Matrix h.

TABLE 3.12. Weights and Pieces, Chemical Goods.

	DESTINATION CITY							
	A	B	C	D	E	F	G	H
B	28 30464 471	size weight pieces	2 27300 525	1 24900 290		1 26100 150	4 32275 428	1 27600 400

size = the sample size
weight = the average weight
pieces = the average number of pieces

TABLE 3.13. Driving Times and Pay Miles, Chemical Goods.

	A	B	C	D	F	G	H
B	8. 21 300	hours pay miles	8. 00 325	14. 00 640	21. 00 860	31. 50 1, 222	8. 00 320

TABLE 3.14. Mean Loading and Unloading Costs, Chemical Goods.

	A	B	C	D	F	G	H
B	$16. 06	–	12. 58	13. 68	14. 90	15. 83	15. 46

TABLE 3.15. Imputed Costs, Chemical Goods.

	A	B	C	D	E	G	H
B	29. 64	total	23. 45	49. 28	61. 06	92. 59	19. 20
	16. 75	tractors	12. 40	22. 40	30. 10	48. 35	11. 20
	9. 70	trailers	7. 80	20. 48	12. 90	28. 64	4. 80
	3. 19	drivers	3. 25	6. 40	18. 06	15. 60	3. 20

Total = Mean Total Imputed Costs
Tractors = Mean Imputed Costs to Tractors
Trailers = Mean Imputed Costs to Trailers
Drivers = Mean Imputed Costs to Drivers

137